ATOMIC POWER

a
SCIENTIFIC
AMERICAN
book

SIMON AND SCHUSTER · NEW YORK

PUBLISHED BY SIMON AND SCHUSTER, INC.
ROCKEFELLER CENTER, 630 FIFTH AVENUE
NEW YORK 20, N. Y.

SEVENTH PRINTING
MANUFACTURED IN THE UNITED STATES OF AMERICA
PRINTED BY MURRAY PRINTING COMPANY
LIBRARY OF CONGRESS CATALOG CARD NUMBER: 55-12530

TABLE OF CONTENTS

INTRODUCTION vii

1. POWER REACTORS

I. THE NUCLEAR REACTOR *by Leon Svirsky* 3
II. RESEARCH REACTORS *by Lawrence R. Hafstad* 15
III. THE BREEDER REACTOR *by E. P. Rosenbaum* 30
IV. POWER REACTORS *by Alvin M. Weinberg* 34
V. THE GENEVA CONFERENCE *by Robert A. Charpie* 53

Atomic fission now joins fire as a source of power for the world's work. From the first Chicago pile, of a dozen years ago, the technology has advanced in the U. S. to the point where five quite different and sophisticated types of nuclear reactor are being tried as generators of useful power. The crux of the future is the breeder reactor, which will make more fissionable material than it burns.

2. RESOURCES

I. THE EARTH'S URANIUM *by Paul F. Kerr* 69
II. URANIUM FROM COAL *by Ralph L. Miller and James R. Gill* 78

In power terms, the world has as much uranium and thorium as coal, two thousand years' supply at the present rate of energy demand. The resources of America, uncovered by diligent prospecting, now bulk large in this calculation. There are important deposits in the lignite beds of the Midwest which reflect the tendency of plants to concentrate uranium from the soil.

3. FUEL AND FISSION PRODUCTS

I. REACTOR CHEMISTRY *by John F. Flagg and Edwin L. Zebroski* 85
II. FISSION PRODUCTS *by Paul J. Lovewell* 92

A reactor is "poisoned," and the chain reaction stops, before one per cent of the fuel has been consumed. Efficient utilization of fuel will

require constant recycling through chemical processes to remove the contaminating fission products and recover the new fissionable material generated by breeder reactors. It may be that the industrial value of the fission products alone will pay for the processing of fuel.

4. ECONOMICS AND POLITICS

Different industries, communities and countries will pay different prices for power. This suggests that atomic power will make its impact piecemeal, arriving first where its "costless fuel" gives it primary market advantage. Its immediate competitive promise is indicated by the recent revision of the U. S. atomic energy statutes and the U. S. proposal for an international atomic energy pool.

5. RADIOBIOLOGY

While atomic weapons carry the additional menace of blast and heat, radiation is a hazard that attends even the most peaceful and constructive use of atomic power. Radiant energy takes lethal effect by deranging the processes of life at many points. For the biologist the rare or radioactive isotopes of elements that occur in organic compounds provide tracers for finding out what goes on inside living things.

6. THERMONUCLEAR REACTIONS

The thermonuclear reactions make the sun and the stars shine. On earth they may now be effected by exposing a quantity of the heavier isotopes of hydrogen to the high temperatures generated in the detonation of a fission bomb. This approach to the engineering of thermonuclear reactions offers little hope of useful power. But other ways may yet be developed to domesticate the thermonuclear reactions.

INTRODUCTION

This is a book about atomic power. That is to say, it deals with the constructive, beneficial or peacetime uses of energy liberated from the atomic nucleus. Most of us, by now, have lost count of the number of atomic bombs that have been detonated. The year 1955, however, saw the first international conference on the peaceful uses of atomic energy convened under the auspices of the United Nations at Geneva. The Geneva Conference, in the words of a contributor to this book, was "the event which opened the door, for all the people of the earth, to the age of nuclear power." Sooner than anyone could have hoped ten years ago, electricity generated by nuclear reactors will be lighting homes and turning the shafts of industry.

Readers of this book will find solid foundation for the promise of Geneva. The wealth of technology in evidence here is assurance that nuclear fission is ready to take its place alongside fire in meeting the increasing energy needs of mankind.

All but two of the chapters were written by authorities closely associated with the topics on which they write. The chapters were first published as articles in the monthly issues of the magazine SCIENTIFIC AMERICAN. *Brought together here, these articles published over a period of several years contribute new relevance to one another and to the large subject with which they are all concerned.*

This book fills an important need. It presents an authoritative account of the information that the layman needs to arrive at intelligent understanding and opinion in this field. Yet nothing in it even approaches secret information or will surprise any well-informed physicist. The book thus demonstrates a number of important facts about atomic power: that nothing really significant in this area can be classified as secret; that it is the monopoly of no single nation; that atomic energy is no more mysterious than electricity or steam and no less natural.

In the first chapter, Leon Svirsky, Managing Editor of SCIENTIFIC AMERICAN, *explains the essential principles of atomic fission and lays a secure foundation for what follows. The "first generation" of nuclear reactors is described by Lawrence R. Hafstad, who was in charge of the Atomic Energy Commission reactor program from 1949 to 1954. These research devices pointed the way at the outset to an extraordinary diversity of promising designs for power reactors. They also set up an agenda of problems, especially those relating to the effects of radiation on materials of construction, with which the technology is primarily concerned today. Five basically different types of power reactor are now under development in the AEC program; their virtues and limitations are described by Alvin M. Weinberg, director of the Oak Ridge National Laboratory. Principal among them is the breeder reactor, the first experimental model of which was built at Arco, Idaho. This reactor sustained a crucial prediction of theory: that a reactor can be made to convert stable isotopes of its fuel element into a larger quantity of fissionable material than it burns in generating power.*

In his account of the work presented at the Geneva Conference, Robert A. Charpie shows that progress in the U. S. has been accompanied by comparable advances abroad. What is more, the disclosure at Geneva of critically important cross-section measurements which the participating nations had previously held secret demonstrated that atomic scientists everywhere have been working on closely parallel lines.

The next section of the book takes up the important question of fuel resources. A few years ago, skeptics were saying that atomic power was not worth the excitement and investment because we would quickly run out of minable uranium. With the addition of thorium to uranium, it is now clear that the supply of nuclear fuel may be placed on a par with coal as an energy resource. Vigorous prospecting has also upset another pessimistic forecast. The U. S., it turns out, has much more uranium than was first thought, including a long-range reserve in the immense lignite beds of Wyoming and the Dakotas.

The calculation of fuel supply is subject to an important variable. This is the question of utilization. The chain reaction in a pile is ultimately stifled by contamination of the fuel with fission products. To restore the fuel and recover the new fissionable material generated in the breeding process will require the constant recycling of the fuel through complex and delicate processes around which a vast new branch of the chemical industry is arising. Chemistry, on top of physics, lays a substantial extra burden of cost on the power produced. This may be offset, however, as industry learns to make use of the fission products and their huge output of radiant energy.

When will atomic power, already technically feasible, become economically important? To discuss this question intelligently, one must add "where" to "when." The cost and the market value of electricity vary widely around the world, as between nations, communities and industries. It is clear that atomic power reactors are not going to sprout everywhere at once. This explains, in part, why nations that pay more for power have been pushing harder on reactor development, while the U. S. has felt able to expend its brains and resources on atomic weapons.

Yet the improving economic prospect, even in the U. S., has now induced a substantial erosion of the "island of socialism" created by the original Atomic Energy Act of 1946. The Act of 1954, reviewed in this book by David F. Cavers of the Harvard Law School, opens the $14 billion public domain of atomic energy at *many points to exploitation by private enterprise. Another indicator, both in the U. S. and abroad, was the U. S. proposal in 1954 of an international pool of technology and resources to be administered by the United Nations. From his survey of work in Europe, Donald J. Hughes of the Brookhaven National Laboratory concludes that the U. S. will find itself engaged in trade, not aid.*

The arrival of atomic power as a major world industrial enterprise introduces a new public health hazard. This is the lethal effects of radiation. The profound relationship between the processes of life and the physics of ordinary matter is demonstrated in the chapter by Edward Spoerl on the insidious ways in which radiant energy may derange the functioning of the living cell. Physics has another relationship to biology, as Martin D. Kamen of Washington University shows. He is one of the scientists who have been using tracers, or "tagged atoms," to find out what goes on inside living organisms.

The last section sounds a different chord. The discovery of the fission reaction has made it possible to trigger the thermonuclear or fusion reactions by which the energy of stars is generated. In the hydrogen bomb, these thermonuclear reactions are the principal single menace to the continued progress of atomic power, and much else besides. When the articles reprinted in this section of the book were written, thermonuclear technology was the exclusive province of the weaponeer, and there was a despairing disposition to believe it always would be. Now, however, it is apparent that we must eventually reckon with power as well as violence from the fusion reaction. At Geneva, the United States, Britain and India revealed that their atomic-energy establishments are working on ways to ignite these reactions under control for peaceful uses.

THE EDITORS *

* Board of Editors: Gerard Piel (Publisher), Dennis Flanagan (Editor), Leon Svirsky (Managing Editor), George A. W. Boehm, Robert Emmett Ginna, Jean Le Corbeiller, James R. Newman, E. P. Rosenbaum, James Grunbaum (Art Director).

PART 1 POWER REACTORS

I. THE NUCLEAR REACTOR
by Leon Svirsky

Leon Svirsky is Managing Editor of SCIENTIFIC AMERICAN.

II. RESEARCH REACTORS
by Lawrence R. Hafstad

As the first director of Reactor Development Division of the U. S. Atomic Energy Commission, Lawrence R. Hafstad was the administrator immediately responsible for the work he reports in this chapter. He was born in Minneapolis in 1904, took his undergraduate degree in physics at the University of Minnesota and his doctorate at The Johns Hopkins University in Baltimore. In 1931, he shared the $1,000 award of the American Association for the Advancement of Science with Merle Tuve for their work on the one-million-volt vacuum tube. He has had a varied industrial, academic and governmental career, as a Bell System engineer, director of research of The Johns Hopkins Applied Physics Laboratory and as research co-ordinator for the Department of Defense. He is now vice-president and director of research of the General Motors Corporation.

III. THE BREEDER REACTOR
by E. P. Rosenbaum

E. P. Rosenbaum is a member of the Board of Editors of SCIENTIFIC AMERICAN.

IV. POWER REACTORS
by Alvin M. Weinberg

At the University of Chicago, where he secured his bachelor's degree and then his doctorate in 1939, Alvin M. Weinberg aimed to do research in biophysics. He was diverted from that ambition on the day after Pearl Harbor, when he was recruited to work "on a half-time basis" on the uranium problem. With the Manhattan District, during the war years, Weinberg helped on the design of the Hanford reactors under the direction of Eugene Wigner. He was research director of the Oak Ridge National Laboratory from 1946 until last year, when he was appointed director of the Laboratory.

V. THE GENEVA CONFERENCE

by Robert A. Charpie

At the age of 30, Robert A. Charpie is assistant director of research at the Oak Ridge National Laboratory. He represents a new generation—probably the third—in nuclear physics. While the second generation was working on the atomic bomb during World War II, Charpie, a Cleveland boy, was serving in the infantry in Italy. He returned to the U. S. in 1946 and attended the Carnegie Institute of Technology. He also took a D.Sc. in theoretical physics there in 1950, having in the meantime worked as a physicist at the Westinghouse Research Laboratories. He joined the Oak Ridge National Laboratory in 1950. As scientific secretary to the Geneva International Conference on the Peaceful Uses of Atomic Energy, Charpie was instrumental in setting up the Geneva meeting and in building its most popular exhibit—the swimming-pool reactor.

THE NUCLEAR REACTOR

by Leon Svirsky

HISTORY MAY DATE the atomic age from the explosion of the first atomic bomb at Alamogordo on July 16, 1945, but mankind will be far happier to date it from the day when the first plant is built to harness nuclear fission for constructive power. The physics of atomic power and the problems that must be solved are neither so recondite, nor so secret, but that any intelligent citizen can understand them.

The entire atomic energy enterprise rests ultimately on one basic reaction—the splitting of uranium 235, one of the lighter isotopes of the heavy element uranium, as the result of its capture of a neutron. Actually it is not U-235 itself that splits but an extremely short-lived daughter, U-236, formed when the neutron is added to the parent. U-236 is so unstable that it cracks almost instantly, within millionths of a second, into two nearly equal parts, recognizable as lighter elements in the middle of the periodic table. These product elements are not always the same; some 40 to 45 species of atoms have been identified as fission products. The combined weight of the two atoms into which the uranium atom splits is less than that of the parent; the lost mass of the annihilated matter is converted into energy, mainly in the form of gamma rays and the kinetic energy of the flying fragments. And the fission products themselves are highly unstable, i.e., radioactive, giving off particles and energy until they decay into stable forms. The energy released by the fission of a single uranium atom is 200 million electron volts. For the purposes of a chain reaction, however, the most important product of the fission process is the release of free neutrons for the production of further fissions.

Uranium fission is not a man-made phenomenon; it can occur in nature. U-235, though a rare species, is present in all natural uranium in the proportion of one part to 139 parts of the common isotope U-238. Occasionally a U-235 atom in uranium-bearing rocks may capture a stray neutron. It fissions, releasing energy and new neutrons. But the probability that these neutrons will be captured by other U-235 atoms and produce further fissions is so small as to be practically nonexistent. And the reasons for this are at the heart of all the problems and difficulties in developing a practical power reactor.

The first reason is that neutrons are exceedingly eligible for capture by nearly all kinds of matter. Most elements, especially the heavier ones, have a strong affinity for neutrons and greedily absorb them. In the rocks any neutrons produced by an accidental fission have an almost infinitely greater chance of being absorbed by the abundant other materials present than by another rare U-235 atom. Consequently, the first step in building a chain-reacting pile, or reactor, is to refine natural uranium, removing all the impurities that would absorb neutrons profitlessly. A chain reaction can be maintained in a pile of uranium oxide because oxygen is a poor absorber of neutrons, but in that case also the compound must be exceedingly pure.

The second problem is that, in uranium itself, fissionable U-235 is at a double disadvantage in its competition for neutrons with U-238. Not only are the U-238 atoms much more abundant but they intercept neutrons at a more likely speed. When neutrons are released by a fission, they are traveling at very high velocity. At this high speed no type of atom has a high probability of capturing them. U-238 absorbs neutrons of intermediate speeds; there is a certain resonance velocity at which it gobbles them up. U-235, on the other hand, is partial to slow neutrons; it captures them most readily when they move at so-called thermal velocities, that is, the normal rate of vibration of the atoms in a solid. Obviously the neutrons are likely to be absorbed by U-238 at intermediate speeds before they can slow down to the thermal speed favored by the rare fissionable atoms. One way to get around the difficulty, of course, is to get rid of the U-238 and use almost pure U-235, as in the bomb. U-235 *can* capture fast neutrons (though with a lower probability), and if there is little U-238 present to take them out of circulation, the chain reaction can proceed. But the separation of U-235 is costly; practical economics demands that a reactor operate, if possible, on natural uranium. A chain reaction can be established in natural uranium by slowing down the fast neutrons quickly so that as many as possible will arrive at the thermal speed favored by U-235 before they can be absorbed by U-238. This is the function of the moderator in a reactor. Its job is to brake the neutrons from millions of electron volts (the physicist's measure of neutron speed) to less than three hundredths of an electron volt within a foot or two.

The material used as moderator (1) must not absorb neutrons and (2) must be light in mass. The neutrons are slowed by a series of collisions with the nuclei of the atoms in the moderator. The reason why these atoms must be light can be illustrated by comparing the particles to billiard balls. A billiard ball that hits a much more massive object than itself (e.g., a large iron ball) rebounds with little loss of speed; it is slowed most when it collides with a body of about its own size, such as another billiard ball. In a reactor the nuclei of light atoms are effective in slowing neutrons because they are comparatively close to the weight of a neutron, which has about the mass of a hydrogen atom.

The materials that come closest to fulfilling the specifications for an ideal moderator are pure carbon (graphite), the light metal beryllium, and heavy water—ordinary water will not do because common hydrogen is an avid neutron-absorber, whereas the heavy hydrogen isotope (H^2) in heavy water, which already has a neutron, is not.

In the actual construction of a reactor, thin rods of pure natural uranium perhaps an inch in diameter, encased in aluminum (a weak absorber of neutrons) to prevent oxidation, are inserted into blocks of graphite. Most of the fast neutrons produced by fissions in such a uranium rod escape from the rod into the graphite, and by the time they have traversed this buffer to their next encounter with uranium they are at the thermal speeds that favor their selective capture by U-235. This is the pile type of reactor, so called because it is a block built up as a lattice of uranium and graphite. While the name "pile" has commonly been used for all types of chain-reacting systems except bombs, "reactor" is now preferred as a more inclusive term, covering the newer types. A reactor using heavy water as moderator, for example, is not strictly a pile but an assembly in which rods of uranium are immersed in a tank of heavy water.

The third basic factor that bars a chain reaction in nature and controls the design of a reactor is the escape of neutrons from the system itself. To retain enough neutrons to keep the reaction going, the reactor must be built to a certain minimum size, so that the volume in which the neutrons are held is large in proportion to the surface from which they may escape. Obviously the necessary size depends on the shape of the system. A sphere, having the smallest surface area for its volume, is the most efficient shape and permits the smallest critical size. A cube is nearly as good. The minimum size is also governed by several other considerations—the degree of enrichment of the uranium with U-235, the kind and amount of moderator, the amount of other materials inserted into the reactor, and so on. The critical size of a reactor consisting of almost pure U-235, such as the bomb, may be very small, perhaps the size of a softball; on the other hand, some of the low-energy reactors are bulky—of the order of 40 feet in diameter including their seven-foot-thick concrete shielding. Thus size itself is no measure of the power of a reactor.

In an atomic bomb the escape of neutrons presents a special problem, for the neutrons and exploding atoms must be held together long enough for the chain reaction to get well under way before the whole system blows apart. This is accomplished by enclosing the bomb in a casing of very dense material that retards the bomb burst and reflects some neutrons back into the system. This suggests one of the obvious avenues for research in the future development of power reactors: the finding of more effective reflectors of neutrons. The invention of a suitable reflecting material that would hold most of the neutrons within the working part of a reactor would not only reduce the critical size of the reactor but would greatly decrease the shielding now required to protect personnel against escaping neutrons. Thus it would enhance the possibility of building compact nuclear engines for ships, planes and vehicles.

The simple principles thus far described are the basis for the design and operation of all present reactors. In operation the pile type of reactor is controlled simply by inserting bars of a material, usually cadmium, that readily absorbs neutrons. By taking neutrons out of circulation, they can bring the chain reaction into equilibrium or stop it entirely. The bars slide into pockets in the interior of the reactor. To start the reactor, all the bars are withdrawn. The chain reaction develops rapidly; its control would be extremely difficult but for the fortunate fact that some of the neutrons released by fission—about one per cent—are delayed in emission from a few seconds to a minute. This gives the system enough inertia so that the operator, working with dials that operate the motors, has ample time to bring the controls into play as the reactor heats up. One bar suffices to regulate the level of the chain reaction. When the reaction reaches the desired level, the operator stabilizes it by inserting the bar to a length that soaks up enough neutrons so that from each fission one and only one neutron is captured by another U-235 atom to continue the reaction. The power level of the reactor is determined by the number of atoms fissioning at any moment at that equilibrium stage. Reactor technicians designate this rate of operation as the "neutron flux," meaning the number of neutrons passing through a given section of the pile per second. In most reactors the ionization chambers, as a safety measure, control extra rods which would drop automatically into the pile if the human operators failed and the reactor rose to a dangerous level. A pile could not possibly approach the energy of a bomb; at worst, if all controls failed and the reactor blew up, it would simulate a rather bad steam-boiler explosion.

If U-235 were the only fissionable material, there would be no hope for uranium power plants except as an experimental curiosity; the isotope is too rare to be seriously considered as a fuel for economical, large-scale use. The hopes for nuclear power lie in the fact that it is possible to manufacture two other fissionable materials: 1) plutonium, derived from U-238, and 2) U-233, a synthetic uranium isotope derived from the heavy natural element thorium.

Plutonium is produced by this series of reactions: A U-238 atom, upon absorbing a neutron in a reactor, becomes U-239. This short-lived isotope (half-life: 23 minutes) promptly emits a beta particle (electron) from its nucleus, gains an electron in its outer shell, and is transformed to the artificial element neptunium 239. Neptunium also is unstable (half-life: 2.3 days) and it in turn expels a beta particle, plus gamma rays, and becomes plutonium 239. Plutonium is fissionable in the same way as U-235; when it captures a neutron it splits in two with a vast yield of energy, possibly greater than that from the fission of U-235.

The thorium chain is this: Thorium 232 absorbs a neutron and becomes the short-lived isotope thorium 233 (half-life: 23 minutes), which emits a beta particle and is transmuted to protoactinium 233 (half-life: 27 days), which in turn loses another beta particle and becomes uranium 233. U-233, like U-235 and plutonium, fissions by capture of a neutron. To start this series of reactions, thorium would have to be mixed in a pile with U-235 as the source of neutrons. Thus the manufacture of both plutonium and U-233 depends basically upon U-235 as the spark plug. But the great promise of these reactions is that they add comparatively abundant U-238 and thorium to U-235 as potential fuels, and the fissionable materials made from them, once formed, become additional sources of neutrons.

As we have seen, a reactor using natural uranium is deliberately designed to make most of the neutrons by-pass absorption by U-238 in order to maintain the chain reaction. But some neutrons inevitably are absorbed by some U-238 atoms, and there is always at least a small surplus of neutrons that makes this possible without stopping the chain. Thus even in a reactor running at a very low power level a little plutonium is created in the uranium rods. To increase the production of plutonium, the power level must be raised: obviously the greater the number of fissioning atoms, the more plutonium will be made. This is the basis of operation of the plutonium-producing piles at Hanford. They are built of pure natural uranium and graphite, like other thermal reactors, but run at considerably higher power levels. Periodically the uranium rods are removed and the plutonium in them is extracted by chemical methods.

By now the dimensions of the power problem begin to become apparent. It is easy enough to calculate that one pound of fissionable fuel contains 10 million kilowatt-hours of energy and is the equivalent of 2.6 million pounds of coal. It is even no great feat to design the outline of a fission power plant: One simply constructs a hot reactor enclosed by a reflector and shield, pipes a coolant (cooling fluid or gas) through it to extract the heat, and transfers the heat to a boiler and steam turbine or a gas turbine. But there are certain difficulties about details.

For instance, the reactor must be raised to temperatures far above any yet attempted under control. Even the "hot" piles at Hanford operate well below the boiling point of water. By attaching the necessary heat-exchanging equipment to one of these reactors and allowing it to go to a high level, power might be generated to light an electric-light bulb or perform a slightly more burdensome task. But it would be the labor of a mountain to produce a mouse. And it would ruin the pile.

The paradox of the vast energy in uranium is that its very concentration constitutes one of the prime problems in extracting power efficiently from it. Its power potential is fantastic; in a bomb the temperature produced is measured in millions of degrees. But pound for pound, uranium is the most expensive of all possible fuels, and its use is prohibitive unless a way is found to apply an appreciable part of the power it is capable of producing in a small space. This raises a number of serious difficulties. One is the heat question. Obviously, to approach any reasonable efficiency in the extraction of nuclear energy means going to very high temperatures. But the vulnerability of materials to heat imposes a relatively low limit on practical operation. The most resistant known materials will tolerate no more than 2,000 degrees Fahrenheit. Reactor designers must consider the effects of heat on all the reactor ingredients—pipes, coolant, moderator, controls, reflectors, the fuel itself. Even more troublesome than the heat problem is the fact that the high neutron flux that develops in a hot reactor also is destructive to materials, especially metals. And materials that may tolerate high temperatures do not withstand particle radiations. All these lessons were expensively learned in the experience with the Hanford piles, which approached a breakdown after the war.

Still another materials problem is that introduced by contamination of the reactor with the pipes and coolant necessary to extract its heat. They divert neutrons from the chain reaction. Even if materials that absorb few neutrons are found for these purposes, at best they will impair the reactor's delicately balanced neutron economy.

Thus the materials question injects a whole galaxy of new problems into power-reactor construction. The answers will require not only engineering studies but new fundamental knowledge in physics and chemistry. Kenneth S. Pitzer, director of the AEC's Division of Research, observed: "We need entirely unprecedented materials, not merely improvements of those already known."

Yet materials constitute but one of many hurdles that must be cleared to make a power reactor economically feasible. Just as important is the conservation of the costly uranium fuel. A reactor run at a high level quickly becomes poisoned by its own fission products. They absorb neutrons. Moreover, in a natural uranium pile operated for power the proportion of U-235 would soon drop to a level where it could not maintain a profitable chain reaction in the contaminated fuel. The poisoned and diluted uranium probably would have to be removed after but a small part, perhaps one per cent, of its fissionable atoms had been used. Should the uranium be reprocessed by chemical removal of the fission products and returned to the pile? That would be a costly process, because the chemical treatment of the highly radioactive material must be carried on by remote control. Should the reactor be enriched with booster portions of fissionable material? Should it be operated on slow neutrons, intermediate neutrons (less moderator) or fast neutrons (no moderator)? These are the principal questions that the Commission is investigating.

The answers to these questions are now being developed in tests of an idea upon which the future of atomic power ultimately depends. This is the "breeder" reactor, which produces new fissionable atoms as fast as it uses the old ones up. The first reactor of this type in the U. S., correctly described by the AEC as a "milestone in the history of atomic power," was brought into operation at Arco, Idaho (see pages 30-33).

The theory of the breeder reactor rests upon the fact that when a U-235 atom fissions, at least two neutrons are produced. The average is between two and three; the possibility is not excluded that it may be more than three. Suppose that a reactor could be built so efficiently that from every fission two neutrons were available for useful capture. One would be taken by a U-235 atom and produce a fission and energy. The other would be absorbed by a U-238 atom and produce an atom of fissionable plutonium. Thus the reactor, while producing energy for power, would constantly replenish the supply of fuel and source of neutrons. If more than two usable neutrons can be realized from each fission, the reactor will actually produce more fissionable material than it consumes.

In such a reactor a blanket of natural uranium around the fissioning material absorbs the excess neutrons and is converted into fuel. By recovering the fissionable plutonium so manufactured and adding natural uranium to the reactor from time to time, it should be possible to keep the reactor going indefinitely. And thorium, it has been found, can serve as well as uranium, for the original capital investment of U-235 or plutonium can be used to convert thorium into U-233, which is also a fissionable isotope and can thus continue the production of power and the transformation of thorium into fuel.

The AEC has reported encouraging results from the experiments at Arco, and additional breeder reactors are now under design and construction. But it is still true, as the AEC General Advisory Committee of scientists reported earlier, that the "engineering difficulties associated with breeding are enormous." To achieve the goal of two usable neutrons per fission requires the reduction of neutron losses in and from the reactor to an extremely low level. On the other hand, the requirements for a power reactor—high operating level, coolant system, and so on—tend to increase the loss of neutrons. Moreover, the chemical recovery of the new fuel bred in the uranium or thorium blanket will be no small job, as Messrs. Flagg and Zebroski explain in their chapter on this tricky subject.

Is there enough available uranium in the world to make the struggle to develop its power potentialities worth while? Investigations indicate that the answer is clearly yes. If breeding works, all of the fairly abundant U-238 and thorium that can be extracted from the earth can be converted into fissionable fuel. The known deposits of uranium ores of commercial grade (at least one per cent uranium) contain an estimated 100 million pounds of uranium —in terms of contained energy that would be enough to supply the entire power needs of the world for at least 50 years at the present rate of power consumption from all sources. In addition, the earth contains an equal amount of available thorium. Uranium and thorium together represent a potential wealth of power greater than the world resources of petroleum and perhaps even of the earth's coal.

In view of the multitude of unsolved problems that stand in the path to nuclear power, attempts to forecast whether uranium will compete as a fuel with coal obviously can be little more than guessing games. Early post-bomb estimates by engineers calculated the cost of nuclear power at from 4 to 10 mills per kilowatt-hour, which would place uranium almost on a par with coal and give it an advantage in areas remote from coal sources. But these computations admittedly were based on extremely meager data. There are persons close to the atomic energy program who believe that at best the power project will be an interesting and costly experiment, possibly demonstrating that power reactors may be usable for certain special purposes, but unlikely to prove that uranium is feasible as a common source of energy.

Yet to dismiss the possibility of the constructive use of atomic power at this stage would be as pointless as it would have been a century ago to dismiss Michael Faraday's discovery of the induction of electric currents. The one certainty in science is that it is unpredictable, and the solution of the atomic power problem may well lie along roads still unseen. The discovery, for example, of large-scale uses for the troublesome radioactive fission products would go a long way toward reducing the power cost; properly safeguarded, they might perhaps be used for energy, for killing bacteria, as industrial tracers, and so on. Some investigators envision a homogeneous reactor—one in which the fuel is mixed in solution with the moderator—that would produce power, manufacture fissionable material, reprocess the fuel and remove wastes—all in one continuous circulating system. Some even dream of short-cutting most of the problems by finding a way somehow to convert the nuclear radiations in a reactor directly into electricity instead of heat.

The goal of economically useful power is the heart of the whole atomic enterprise—if one may think of peace rather than war. From that point of view the "atomic age" is still in the future. As of 1949, the AEC hoped to produce a functioning power reactor in five to ten years and an economically practical one in twenty years. The first of these objectives is now in sight. The future, however, depends as much on politics as on research. For it is idle to pretend that atomic bomb-making does not seriously impede the development of atomic energy for peaceful purposes. "Guns-or-butter" issues arise at many points—in the budget, the use of uranium, the recruitment of personnel, security restrictions, the control of research.

RESEARCH REACTORS

by Lawrence R. Hafstad

NUCLEAR REACTORS are the machines for converting the energy of nuclear fission into forms that can be turned to useful purposes. They are large, complicated, expensive and controversial. They provide man with the most concentrated energy source thus far devised, and in the imagination, at least, they have unlimited possibilities. The uses proposed for them have ranged from performance of the world's drudgery to the powering of rockets for space travel. Some of the proposed uses are strictly figments of the imagination. But reactors themselves, as a new type of machine with new potentialities, are a functioning reality, and it is now possible to discuss some of them publicly in considerable detail. Much of the information on the construction and performance of eight early reactors, five of which are in the U. S., has been declassified by agreement between the U. S., Britain and Canada.

In the preceding chapter, Leon Svirsky discussed the principles of nuclear power and indicated some of the problems that face the atomic engineer. To show how the principles are being applied and how the problems are being met, this report will briefly describe three of the "first generation" of reactors built in the U. S. Our experience with these reactors has laid the foundations for our present and future progress toward economically useful atomic power.

Not the least striking feature of reactors is the great variety of possible designs. This is one of the things that makes them so different from the power plants that we have been used to. Conventional coal-burning furnaces, for example, are all generally recognizable as belonging to a common genus; they may differ in size and details, but essentially they are built and operated on the same fundamental plan. Imagine, however, a furnace variation which for fuel used carbon dioxide, say, instead of coal, which burned its fuel in a medium of water instead of air and which operated in a kettle instead of the usual firebox. That would certainly be a radical variation, but it is no more radical than the variations among the nuclear furnaces called reactors. The three reactors to be described here, all low-power machines used mainly for research, represent three very different types which indicate the wide range of possibilities.

The world's oldest nuclear reactor is the uranium-graphite pile at the University of Chicago in which a chain reaction was first achieved in 1942. This pile, later taken apart and rebuilt at the Argonne National Laboratory near Chicago, is a cube-shaped mass of blocks of graphite containing lumps of natural uranium or uranium oxide in a lattice arrangement; the oxide was used because only a small amount of pure uranium metal was available when the pile was built. The graphite blocks, which act as the moderator and the structural bricks of the pile, are 4⅛ inches square in cross

Natural uranium-graphite reactor in which the first self-sustaining nuclear chain reaction was achieved is shown in this simplified cross section. The reactor was originally built at the University of Chicago and later rebuilt at Argonne National Laboratory. It is basically a large cube of graphite blocks, some of which contain small cylinders of uranium or uranium oxide, as shown in the sketch of part of a layer of graphite blocks below. An outer layer of graphite blocks containing no uranium serves as a neutron reflector. The shaft of blocks sticking up from the top of the main cube in the cross section is the "thermal column," a means by which slow neutrons may be permitted to diffuse out of the reactor for experimental purposes. The wooden structure at the right supports control rods and stringers that may be inserted into the cube; the holes in the front of the cube permit the insertion of safety rods.

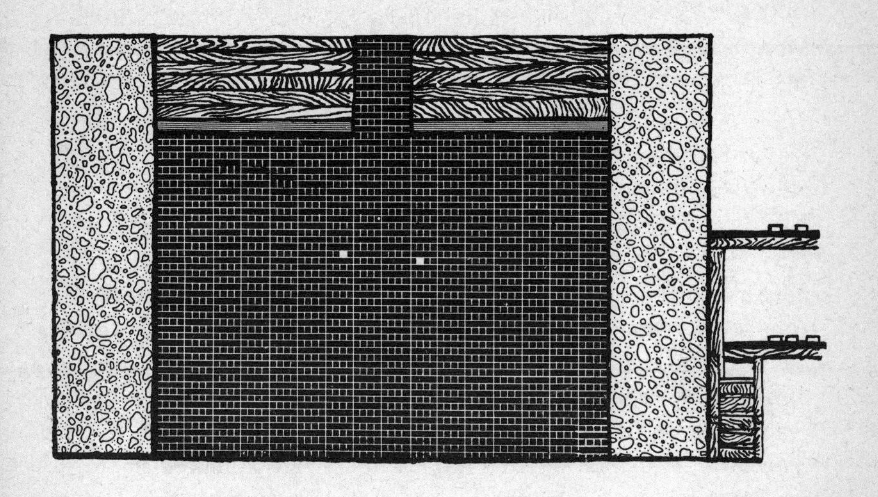

CONCRETE
WOOD
LEAD
GRAPHITE

section and of various lengths, usually 16½ inches. Some of the blocks have holes bored in them at intervals 8¼ inches apart. In these are inserted the uranium lumps, each a cylinder 2¼ inches in diameter and about six pounds in weight. The uranium-loaded blocks are called "live." The solid graphite blocks without uranium are known as "dead" graphite; they are used for spacing and neutron-reflecting purposes. The pile was built up, layer by layer, with alternating layers of live and dead blocks. It became "critical," i.e., started a self-sustaining chain reaction, when the fiftieth layer was laid on. Four layers of dead blocks were then laid on top as a reflector, and over this went a cover of six inches of lead and about four feet of wood. The sides of the pile were surrounded with a similar reflecting barrier of at least twelve inches of dead graphite and with protective walls of concrete five feet thick.

When completed, the pile measured 30 feet wide, 32 feet long and 21.5 feet high and had a total weight of more than 1,400 tons. It contained approximately 52 tons of uranium, in 3,200 lumps of the pure metal and 14,500 lumps of uranium oxide.

Openings were provided in the pile for five control rods 17 feet long. They are bronze strips covered with cadmium, an excellent absorber of neutrons. Three of the rods are automatic safety controls; they are equipped with 100-pound weights that quickly pull them into the pile in the event of electrical power failure or other emergency. The operating level, or power, of the pile is controlled

Heavy-water reactor at Argonne National Laboratory is shown in a simplified cross section. In this reactor the neutrons produced by fission are moderated by heavy water instead of graphite. The heavy water is contained in an aluminum tank approximately six feet across and nine feet high. Suspended in the tank are 120 uranium rods. Around the tank is a layer of graphite to reflect escaping neutrons. Around the graphite is a layer of lead-cadmium alloy and a heavy shield of concrete. At the top of the tank is a layer of lead; beneath it is a thin layer of cadmium, and between the cadmium and the heavy water is a layer of helium. Toward the right side of the tank is a

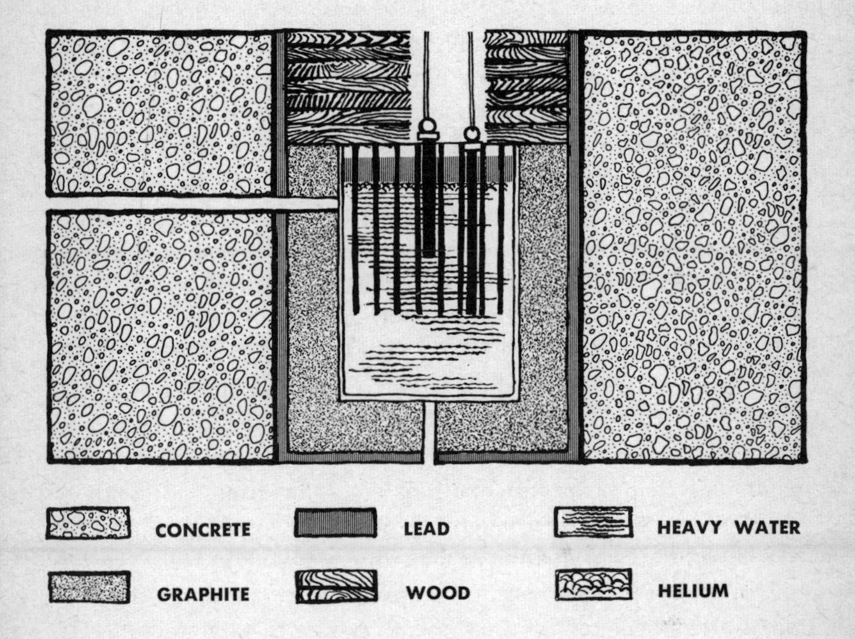

control rod. In the middle of the tank is the "experimental thimble," a device for inserting experimental materials into the reactor. Above the tank is a layer of wood and steel. The heat generated by the reactor must be dissipated; this is accomplished by circulating the heavy water through a heat exchanger, not shown here. Among other details not shown by this cross section are two horizontal columns of graphite that pass through the concrete shielding. One of these is to insert experimental materials into the reactor; the other, to permit a beam of slow neutrons to pass out of it. The reactor can handle 32 neutron irradiations simultaneously.

by a single rod which is moved in or out to regulate the neutron flux. Because it lacks a cooling system, the maximum safe operating power of this pile is only 200 watts.

The research reactors at Oak Ridge and Brookhaven, and the great production piles at Hanford, are roughly similar to this first reactor. Their mass is largely graphite, and they are fueled by natural uranium. But they have systems for cooling, either by air or water, and therefore can run at higher power levels. They also have devices for loading and unloading fuel without tearing down the reactor. In addition they incorporate a number of other improvements and refinements required to provide dependable control for their much greater power and to serve their different purposes.

The second type of reactor is the heavy-water unit at Argonne. The first version of this machine, which used natural uranium, was also the first of its type in the world. It was built by the Manhattan District during the war because of the remote chance that graphite piles might not be able to produce fissionable material in the amounts needed for bombs. In 1950 it was modified to use enriched uranium. In this reactor heavy water, instead of graphite, is the moderator that slows fast neutrons emerging from the fission of U-235 atoms to the thermal speeds necessary for their capture by U-235 and the continuation of a chain reaction. The following details apply to the reactor as it was run on natural uranium; the principles are unchanged for the present version. In an aluminum tank six feet in diameter and about nine feet high, filled with about 6½ tons of heavy water, are suspended 120 uranium metal rods 1.1 inches in diameter and six feet long. The rods are sheathed in aluminum for protection against corrosion. They are arranged to form a square lattice with 5⅜ inches between their centers. This reactor is smaller than the graphite pile because heavy water is more effective than graphite in slowing neutrons and does not absorb them as readily. Its total weight of uranium is less than three tons, in contrast to the 52 tons in the graphite pile.

The heavy-water reactor tank is surrounded on its bottom and sides by a two-foot neutron reflector of graphite blocks. Around the reflector, in turn, are a four-inch casing of lead-cadmium alloy and then a shield of concrete eight feet thick. The reactor's top shielding consists of a layer of helium gas, a thin layer of cadmium metal, a one-foot layer of lead bricks and finally a four-foot layer of blocks of wood and steel.

Eleven small openings pierce the shield and reflector. These portholes, equipped with removable shielding plugs, are used to measure neutron intensity within the reactor, to insert materials for exposure to neutrons and to let beams of radiation emerge for experiments outside the reactor. There are also three large openings. One is a pocket roughly thirty inches square containing twenty hollow graphite receptacles in which materials can be placed for irradiation. Another is a graphite-plugged aperture five feet square which permits the passage from the reactor of a beam of slow neutrons. The third is a four-inch aluminum pipe inserted in the tank through the top. Into this pipe, known as the central experimental thimble, samples of material may be lowered for exposure to the most intense radiations of both fast and slow neutrons. When all the reactor's openings are used, thirty-two irradiations can be performed simultaneously.

To cool the reactor, the heavy water circulates between the tank and an external heat exchanger at the rate of 200 gallons per minute. The cooling system is able to handle about 300 kilowatts of heat. Normally the heavy water is at a temperature of 104 degrees Fahrenheit when it emerges from the tank; after it has passed through the heat exchanger, it is about 14 degrees cooler.

The operator measures and controls all the major aspects of the reactor's operation at panels in a near-by room. To start the machine he pushes a button: this lifts the 32-pound safety rods out of the heavy water. Other buttons control two motor-driven rods that regulate the reactor power level. To shut off the reactor the fuel and the moderator. As a chain reaction develops, the solution heats up; hence the name water boiler.

The first version of this reactor was a low-power model known as LOPO. It had no shielding and reached a power of only a twentieth of a watt. In December 1944, LOPO was replaced by HYPO, a higher-powered model of six kilowatts which went critical with 1.8 pounds of U-235. Its fuel is "enriched"; that is, the uranium in the uranyl salt contains about one part of fissionable U-235 to six parts of U-238, instead of the 1-to-140 ratio in natural uranium.

The heart of this reactor is a one-foot stainless-steel sphere filled with the "soup," a solution of uranyl nitrate. Then comes a reflecting shell, or tamper, consisting of an inner layer of beryllium oxide and a thicker outer layer of graphite. Around this assembly is the shield: four inches of lead, 1/32-inch of cadmium and five feet of poured concrete.

At the working face of the reactor a square tunnel pierces the shield. This tunnel is plugged with graphite to form a column for the passage of slow neutrons. The graphite column and the reflector have a number of ports for experimental irradiations. In addition there is a tube one inch in diameter that penetrates into the heart of the reactor itself. Through this tube, which Los Alamos workers call the "Glory Hole," materials can be thrust into the sphere for exposure to a very high flux of neutrons.

The operation of HYPO presents some special problems. Cooling is accomplished easily enough by circulating water, at the rate of about 50 gallons per hour, through a coiled tube in the central sphere. But the highly ionized atoms produced by fissions in the reactor decompose the water in the fuel solution into an explosive mixture of hydrogen and oxygen gas, at the rate of about half a cubic foot of gas per hour. Moreover, the radiations also produce a small volume of highly radioactive gases. Consequently the design has to provide a means for constantly diluting and flushing out these gases.

the remaining necessary "secrets" could be uncovered and the real atomic era ushered in. Actually the atomic bomb problem and the civilian power problem have little in common except the language. They differ in kind rather than in degree.

The bomb project was almost uniquely "black and white": it was either a grand success or a colossal failure. The civilian power problem is quite different. Enough technical facts have long been known to assure us that electric power can be produced—if we are willing to pay the price. There is an analogy in the proposition of producing electric power from the winds or the tides. Our technical ability to tap these sources of energy is not questioned. But we don't utilize the wind and the tide because the power so produced would be more costly than that obtained conventionally from coal and oil.

The cost of construction of a nuclear power plant is still essentially unknown. We have not yet designed, much less built and operated, a reactor intended to deliver significant amounts of power economically. Our experience is that in this business estimates cannot be taken at face value and invariably turn out to be too low. My own approach has been to try to find the upper limit for the cost of a power plant, basing this estimate on the firmest available figures on the most nearly similar reactor either already built or under construction. Estimates based on the cost of low-temperature reactors for producing plutonium, on the assumption that they can be redesigned for operation at higher temperatures, cannot be taken seriously.

Perhaps our best yardstick for estimating nuclear power plant costs is provided by the ship propulsion reactor now under construction. The cost of this mobile reactor has been estimated roughly as $1,400 per kilowatt-hour of installed electrical capacity. The corresponding cost of a conventional stationary coal-burning power plant is $100 to $150 per kilowatt-hour capacity. Now we know that many savings can be made in the $1,400 figure for the

mobile nuclear plant. In a plant for civilian power it seems possible that we could avoid some of the high costs involved in developing a prototype reactor, in meeting the Navy's requirements of weight and space, in reprocessing fuels, in the lack of volume production, in the extreme military security precautions and in the extreme precautions for safety of personnel. If we could pick up a factor of two or three through savings in these items and through the technical improvements that will almost certainly come in a field as new as atomic energy, we would begin to close in on the competitive figure of $100 to $150.

The fuel costs are not negligible and are even more uncertain than construction costs. All fissionable material thus far manufactured has been produced by a government monopoly on a high-pressure basis in such a way that precise cost allocations simply cannot be made. Taking from the open literature the figure of $20 per gram for nuclear fuel, we get a fuel cost of one mill per kilowatt-hour, as compared with two mills for coal. The $20 figure is almost certainly low, and it seems likely that it will rise as the supply of high-grade uranium ore runs out. Hence it appears that fuel costs will be about the same for a power plant burning U-235 as for one burning coal, while the cost of the installation, and probably of its operation, will be considerably higher.

The civilian power plant need not, however, confine itself to producing power: it could also produce plutonium. The reactors now producing plutonium throw away their heat—hundreds of thousands of kilowatts of it. Suppose this heat could be put to some useful purpose, say, the production of power, or even the distillation of sea water? What then is the economic picture?

Technically a reactor to produce both power and plutonium is not out of the realm of possibility, but scientists don't know much about such a reactor yet. If one can be made to work, much of the operating cost will be charged oft to the production of the fuel, and the power may be provided at reasonable cost.

Suppose now that either out of AEC laboratories or from industrial contractors there emerges a design of a reactor producing plutonium and yielding electric power as a by-product. Will this finally usher in the atomic era? I am afraid not. The major charges will still be carried by the military need for plutonium. Only if and when civilian power can pay its own way, from the uranium mines to the waste-disposal dump, can it truly be said that the civilian atomic power problem will have been solved. In the meantime we would be less than prudent if we did not take advantage of every opportunity to make the operation of reactors economically practical by increasing emphasis on the use of by-products, whether military or civilian.

THE BREEDER REACTOR

by E. P. Rosenbaum

THE MOST IMPORTANT REACTOR built since the original Chicago pile is the one now designated by the AEC as EBR-1, at Arco, Idaho. Its initials stand for "Experimental Breeder Reactor," and the digit *1* signifies that it is already the progenitor of reactors of more advanced design (see next chapter).

EBR-1 is the first reactor to begin testing the possibility of harnessing atomic energy as an economically competitive source of power. The key to this possibility lies in the reactor's middle name: whether it can be made to breed more fuel than it consumes. Its assignment is to burn the fissionable U-235 in natural uranium and, with the neutrons from these fissions, to convert the much more abundant U-238 in the mixture to fissionable plutonium. The fission of U-235 atoms releases an average of 2.5 neutrons per atom. One of these neutrons must be captured by another U-235 atom to maintain the chain reaction; for breeding to succeed, better than one of the remaining 1.5 neutrons must be captured by U-238 to make plutonium. As Alvin Weinberg explains in the next chapter, other breeding cycles, using plutonium, U-233 and thorium,

Reactor chamber of the Arco experimental breeder reactor is shown close up in this schematic cross section. The chain-reacting core is the football-shaped cross-hatched object in center. It supplies neutrons to the surrounding blanket of U-238. Liquid metal coolant flows through vertical holes in blanket and around core, emerging at upper right with a temperature of 660 degrees Fahrenheit.

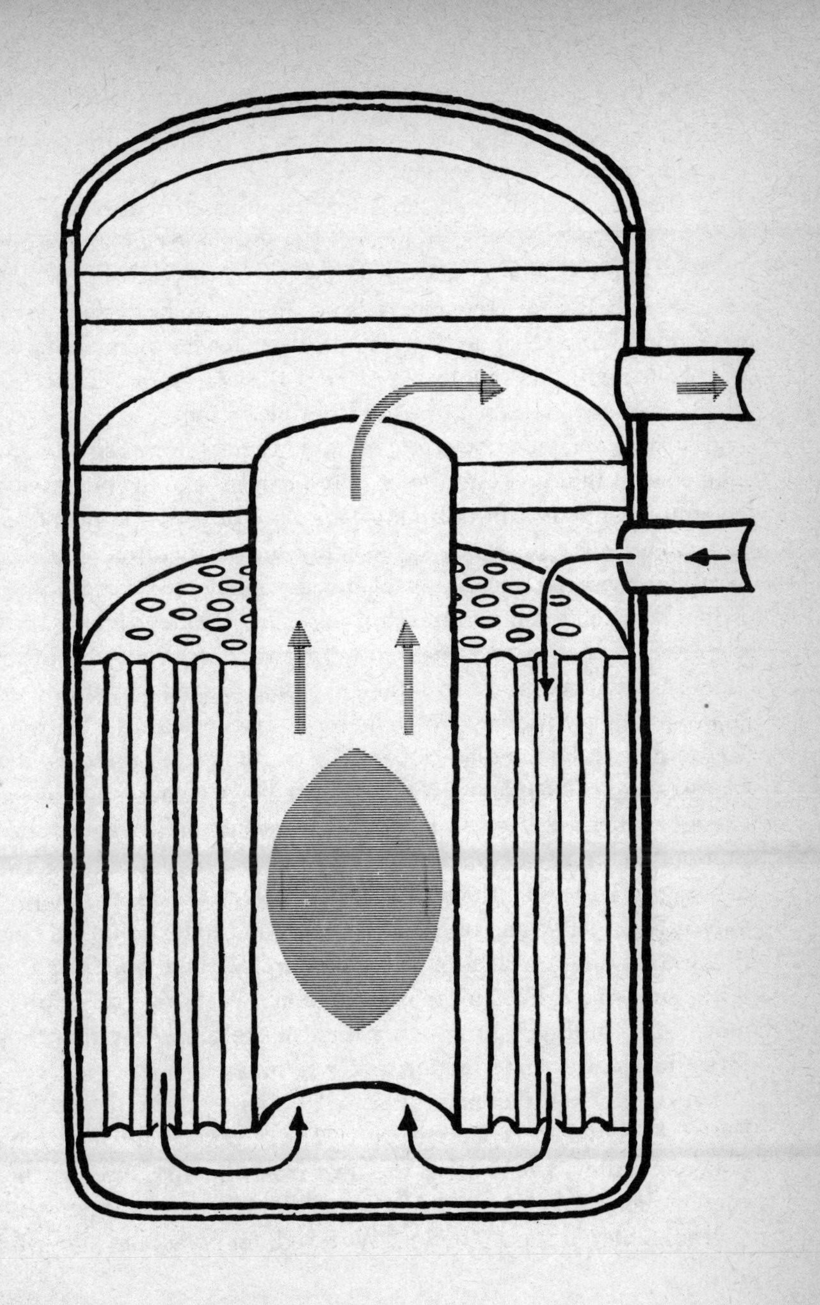

will be tested, perhaps more successfully, in future breeder reactors now under development.

In the design of EBR-1, particular care was taken to cut neutron losses to a minimum and ensure that as many as possible find their way to U-238 atoms. Its reacting core is tiny—about the size of a football. Because the materials used in a reactor to slow down neutrons all absorb some neutrons, this reactor has no moderator: it operates with fast neutrons. Around the core is a "blanket" of U-238, which catches neutrons to form plutonium.

All of the reactor's power is generated as heat in this small core. The coolant that picks up the heat and carries it to the electricity-generating unit is a liquid metal—an alloy of sodium and potassium. This alloy does not appreciably absorb neutrons and has excellent characteristics as a heat transfer medium: for example, it is liquid at room temperature but has a high boiling point, 1,500 degrees. It is, however, extremely active chemically: it burns vigorously when exposed to air and explodes on contact with water. It is also highly radioactive because of its exposure to neutrons. Hence it must be handled carefully. Emerging from the core at a temperature of 660 degrees, the coolant flows through a heat exchanger, where it gives up its heat to a second circuit, and is then pumped to an elevated storage tank, from which it begins its circuit again. To handle the radioactive liquid metal, special pumps, valves, flow meters and other instruments had to be designed. One of these is a unique "electromagnetic pump" without moving parts. It operates much like an induction motor: electromagnetic forces move the liquid metal through a duct in the same way that they force the rotor of an induction motor to turn.

The section of the plant through which radioactive coolant flows is enclosed by a concrete shield. The second circuit of sodium-potassium alloy, which takes the heat from the first, does not become radioactive and is outside the shield. It transfers the heat to a steam boiler of special design. With sodium-potassium alloy and water together in the same apparatus, the boiler must be constructed so that they cannot come into contact with each other.

The reactor core has the highest flux of neutrons known—650 million million neutrons per square inch per second. This creates a severe problem, because a high neutron flux breaks down the physical structure of all materials and equipment exposed to it, including the uranium itself.

The small size of the reactor core raises another serious problem, but one in the more familiar branch of engineering known as heat exchange. The AEC has not disclosed how heat can be transferred efficiently from the very small reactor core. The reactor yields four kilowatts of power for each cubic inch of the core, whereas a modern oil-fired naval boiler gives only six tenths of a kilowatt per cubic inch. Whether four kilowatts per cubic inch can be extracted as heat and power from the core remains a question. Limitations on heat-exchange technique may rule out the fast neutron reactor and hence natural uranium, which requires fast neutrons for the conversion of U-238 to fissionable plutonium, as the combination of choice for the power-generating breeder reactor.

EBR-1 is producing enough power to supply its own electrical machinery. But the AEC as yet has released no data on its performance as a breeder. If breeding does succeed, and despite their cautious tone most authorities believe it will, we may permit ourselves to conjure with the astronomical energy potential of the atomic nucleus. It is pointed out that 20 pounds of natural uranium will yield 51,800,000 kilowatt hours of electricity—enough to light 25,000 average American homes for a year. At an assumed price of $35 per pound for refined uranium, this gives a fuel cost of .0013 mills per kilowatt hour, exclusive of the cost of chemical processing to separate the plutonium. Even if fuel processing raises the cost by a factor of 10, the fuel cost would still be practically negligible.

POWER REACTORS

by Alvin M. Weinberg

WITHIN THE NEXT five years the Atomic Energy Commission will invest $200 million in a program to develop economical nuclear power plants. The Commission is hedging this bet, so to speak, by backing five different reactor plans—a technological sweepstakes quite without precedent. If any one of the five approaches reaches the goal, the reward, of course, will be considerable. But in any case the investment should at least bring us within sight of the objective of harnessing nuclear power on a basis competitive with coal and oil. (Military nuclear engines are a different story.)

Why five separate approaches? Why not one—or twenty? It is no secret that no one line of reactor development has yet given convincing evidence of superior promise. In addition, the various reactor types are in a sense not really competitive because their objectives are not entirely comparable. On the other hand, not even the U. S. is rich enough to investigate every likely possibility. It has often been said that there are as many ideas for reactors as there are reactor designers. The various designers naturally have an emotional attachment to their own designs, or at

Fuel-breeding cycle depends on neutron economy. Of *n* neutrons released when a fissionable atom splits (*top*), one must maintain the chain reaction (*left*), some will be absorbed by nonbreeding materials or escape (*second from right*), and at least one (*two are shown here*) must hit "fertile" Th-232 or U-238 atoms, which decay into U-233 or Pu-239.

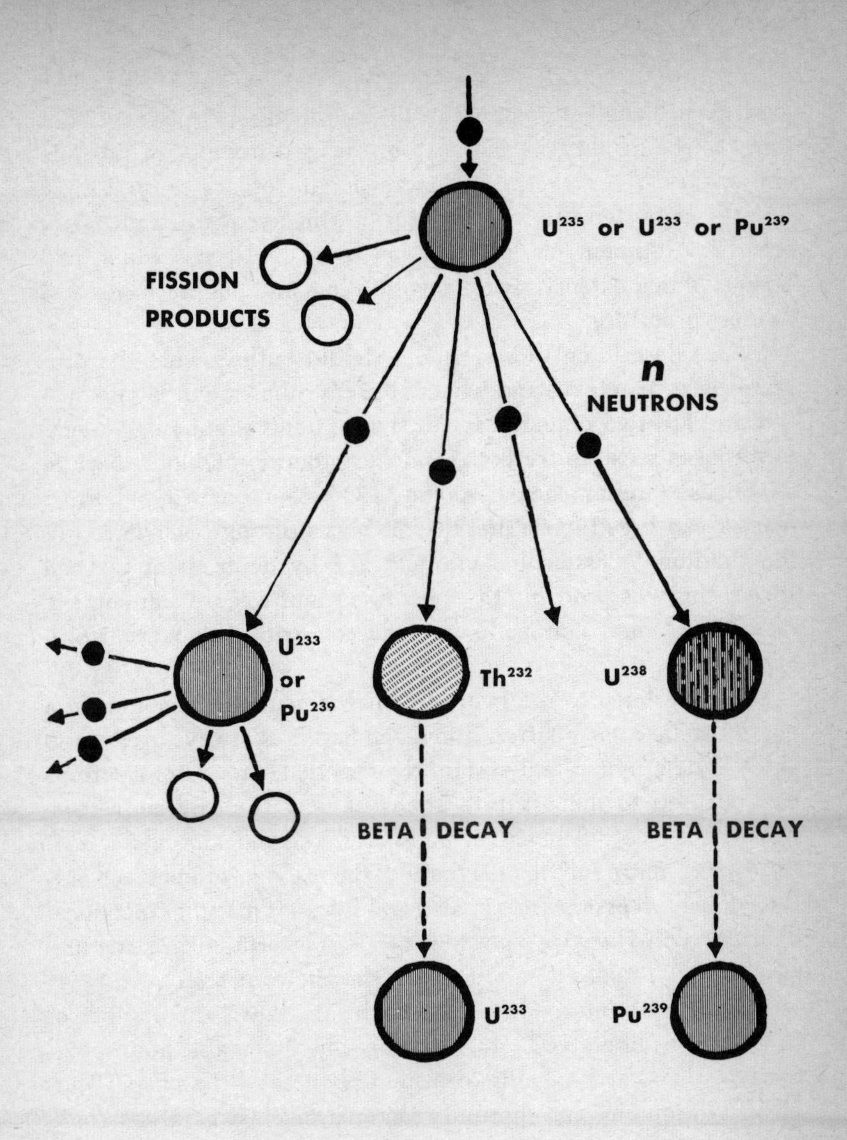

U^{235} or U^{233} or Pu^{239}
FISSION
PRODUCTS
n
NEUTRONS
U^{233}
or
Pu^{239}
Th^{232}
U^{238}
BETA DECAY
BETA DECAY
U^{233}
Pu^{239}

least an attachment colored by their individual experience, but some selection must be made from the vast number of possible approaches. When the Joint Congressional Committee on Atomic Energy requested the AEC to project a five-year program of reactor development, the Commission listed five types which had been explored extensively for several years and had been selected as most promising.

Before describing these types, I should outline what the program seeks to achieve and what materials it has to work with.

There are two potential fuels: thorium and uranium. It therefore makes sense to try both, and the program includes thorium as well as uranium reactors. As the AEC has announced, a thorium reactor can breed more fuel than it burns through conversion of the thorium to fissionable uranium 233 by neutrons of thermal speed; this was probably the most important scientific announcement the Commission made in connection with the five-year program.

Closely related to the matter of fuel is neutron economy. In a chain reaction one neutron from each fission is always used up to cause a new fission and sustain the reaction; any extra neutrons can be used to manufacture atoms of new fuel, by converting uranium 238 into fissionable uranium 235 or thorium into U-233. To "breed" more fuel than is burned, the number of neutrons produced by each fission must exceed two by a fair margin, since some neutrons will always be wasted, say, by absorption in structural materials. This consideration affects the choice of fuel.

According to information released by the AEC, the number of fast neutrons liberated by the fission of any fissionable atom (plutonium, U-233 or U-235) is "considerably greater than two." Thus either a uranium or a thorium reactor using fast neutrons could breed more fuel than it burned. But a fast-neutron reactor is so concentrated and small that it is difficult to cool and control. From the engineering standpoint there is strong incentive to prefer thermal-neutron reactors, for they are much larger and more dilute and therefore much easier to cool. The problem, however, is that the yield of available neutrons is reduced when they are slowed from fast to thermal speed. In the case of plutonium, generated in a uranium reactor, the yield of thermal neutrons per fission is only two. This seems to rule out uranium as the raw material for a thermal breeder. The thermal-neutron yield from U-233, generated in a thorium reactor, is "greater than two." Consequently, thorium is an attractive possibility as the basis of a thermal breeder.

Even a uranium thermal reactor may produce some new fuel during operation, though not at as fast a rate as it burns its fuel. Such a reactor is said to be "regenerative." There is a continuous spectrum of possible regenerative reactors. As long as natural uranium is fairly cheap, and provided the reactor can burn as much as one per cent of all its original uranium atoms without reprocessing, the fuel cost of a nuclear power plant can be low—1.35 mills per kilowatt hour. Such a reactor of course is slightly regenerative, for only .7 per cent of the original atoms is fissionable U-235; the remaining .3 per cent of the fuel burned is plutonium which has been produced by conversion of U-238 through absorption of neutrons.

Another big issue in the reactor competition is the efficiency of the conversion of heat into electricity. This problem centers on the coolant. The most interesting fact here is that three of the five reactor schemes to be explored will use water (ordinary water or heavy water) as the coolant, in spite of the relatively low thermal efficiency inherent in water. The two main reasons are: first, that water is plentiful, and second, and more important, that it is the only common coolant which is also a moderator. An essential simplicity is achieved by combining the two functions of slowing neutrons and cooling in one material. One of the reactor types will take this combining of functions still further by using heavy water as moderator, coolant and carrier of the fuel in solution.

Heavy water, which is the best of all moderators because it absorbs almost no neutrons, offers another advantage: it has a high "material" efficiency which offsets its low thermal efficiency. It can spread out the dissolved uranium atoms in a very dilute solution without capturing many of the neutrons they produce. And as a result of this intimate contact with the fuel, the heavy water should extract the heat from the fissioning fuel very efficiently. Since the fuel is expensive, this highly efficient use of it has much the same effect as high thermal efficiency in lowering the cost of producing electricity.

The sacrifice of thermal efficiency in favor of other efficiencies will apply to many other aspects of the design of nuclear power plants. In fact, it has been estimated that the most economical operating temperature for a nuclear-fueled steam plant will be between 600 and 800 degrees Fahrenheit—considerably lower than the standard in conventional steam plants. The lower-temperature steam system of course will be cheaper to build. It will be feasible if, as seems likely, the relative cost of the nuclear fuel can be reduced to the point where the fuel itself is practically free.

Still another test that nuclear power reactors will have to pass is economy in the processing of their fuel: that is, in dissolving, extracting, recovering and fabricating the metal. Here the most promising approach is the homogeneous reactor, where a continuous recycling of the dissolved fuel, as opposed to expensive batch methods, seems possible. It has already been disclosed that fused salts dissolved in liquid bismuth look promising as extractants of fission products from the fuel.

The entire problem of nuclear power is finally summed up in a single criterion: How many mills per kilowatt hour of electricity? As has been said so often, the costs comprise capital costs, fuel costs and operating costs. If there is any appreciable fuel regeneration, the fuel cost in nuclear plants will be negligible. However, the operating costs, including chemical reprocessing, may be several mills per kilowatt hour. To meet the competition of the best coal-fired steam plants in the U. S., nuclear plants will have to generate power at a cost between 4 and 7 mills, depending on the price of coal in the locality of the plant. Assuming that nuclear fuel is cheap, it will be possible to invest about $100 to $200 per kilowatt more in building the plant and still compete in power cost with a coal plant. The five-year-program reactors, being initial steps, are not themselves expected to achieve this, but it is hoped that they lie on paths of development which will lead to cheap nuclear power.

Now let us consider each of the five types of reactors to be investigated. It is convenient to group them according to their engineering genealogy—i.e., the engineering tradition or development path along which they lie. From this point of view they fall into two groups: those using water as the coolant and those using a liquid metal coolant, such as sodium. Within each category, of course, there are many possible variations: for example, a given type of reactor may use uranium or thorium as the fuel, it may breed or regenerate fuel or operate only on its original charge, and so on. The unknowns being investigated are mainly engineering questions: How practical is sodium as a coolant? How long can a high-pressure radioactive water system be kept leakproof? Will the slightly radioactive turbine or the steam boiler be an important maintenance problem? As the following descriptions show, the reactors are intended primarily to answer such subtle questions of engineering feasibility and economics.

We begin with the pressurized water reactor (PWR) designed by the Westinghouse Electric Corporation for the Duquesne Light Company in Pittsburgh, which will operate the plant. Its principle

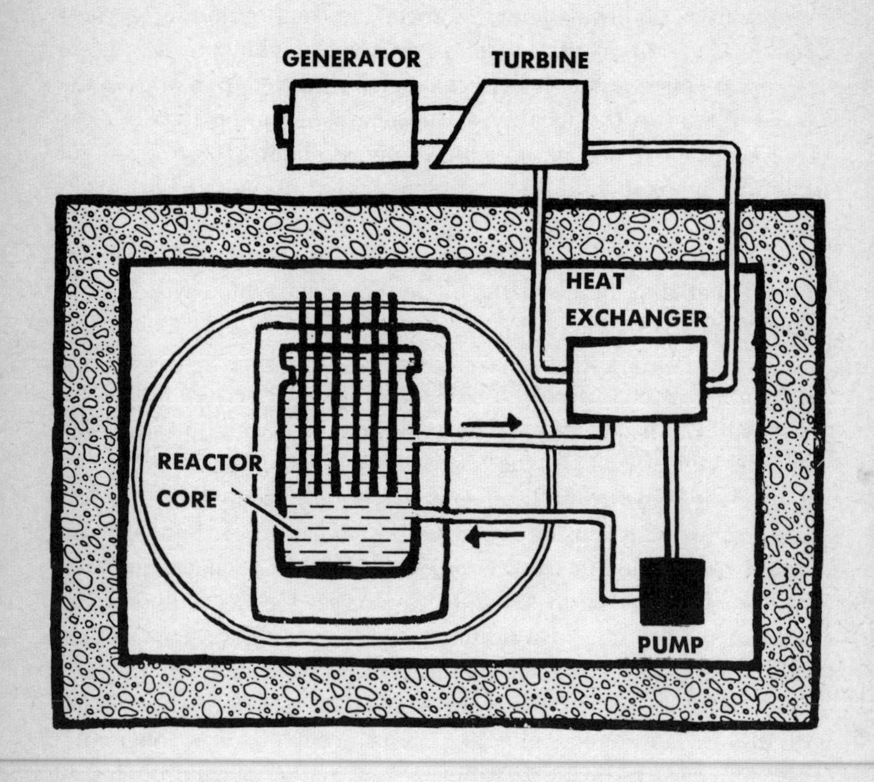

Pressurized water reactor is the type employed by the U.S. Navy in first nuclear-powered submarines. In application to central station power plant, the fuel elements of slightly enriched uranium rods will be coated with a corrosion-resistant metal. More than 10 tons of uranium will be used. A large gas-tight pressurized shell will surround the core assembly and the heat exchanger assemblies. The light-water coolant heated by uranium fission generates steam in the heat exchangers.

is essentially that of the reactors Westinghouse has built for the Navy to power submarines. However, it will use as fuel slightly enriched natural uranium, instead of highly enriched U-235. The core of PWR will generate approximately 300,000 kilowatts of heat, which will be transferred to a heat exchanger by circulating water at a pressure of 2,000 pounds per square inch and a temperature of 525 degrees F. The heat exchanger will produce saturated steam at a pressure of 600 pounds per square inch. This steam in turn will go to a conventional turbine which is expected to generate a net electrical output of more than 60,000 kilowatts.

The high-pressure core will be contained in a carbon-steel vessel nine feet in diameter, coated with stainless steel. The uranium is to be disposed in a tight cluster of metallic fuel elements.

Because the expansion of the water as the temperature goes up allows neutrons to leak out more easily, such a system is inherently self-stabilizing; there is a possibility that PWR will need rather few control rods. The extremely remote possibility of a nuclear runaway is guarded against by enclosing each of the high-pressure components in a stout, gas-tight pressure vessel. The whole reactor system will be underground.

The submarine reactor has demonstrated the practicality of the high-pressure water system and pioneered some of the necessary equipment, such as the famous canned rotor pumps. Thus the PWR is less experimental than the other reactors to be built; in fact, the choice of water cooling and moderation for PWR was dictated by the requirement that the reactor demonstrate reliable nuclear power rather than cheap nuclear power. None of the estimates of cost suggest that PWR will be an economical power producer. However, as one tangible step along the road to a completely rationalized high-pressure water system PWR makes good sense.

Several paths lead from the PWR toward more economical power. For example, the great expense of fabricating the core will fall as automatic techniques for the manufacture of fuel elements are learned. Again, neutron economy can be greatly improved either by using heavy water instead of ordinary water or by replacing the uranium fuel with thorium and U-233. Furthermore, higher thermal efficiency and lower power cost might be realized by raising the pressure.

An obvious way to improve the performance of a water-cooled reactor is to generate turbine steam directly in the core instead of in a separate housing. One circulation loop would be eliminated, and the pressure of the system would be lowered, for the highest pressure in the reactor would be only that in the turbine. This rationalization of pressurized-water philosophy is so attractive that the AEC decided to include a direct-boiling reactor in the five-year program, and it is embodied in the second type: the experimental boiling-water reactor (EBWR) to be built by Argonne National Laboratory. Like PWR it will use slightly enriched uranium. There appears to be no reason, however, why thorium could not be used in the direct-boiler design. In that case this reactor might come close to breeding, especially if the moderator-coolant were heavy water. Ordinary water was chosen for EBWR because of the present difficulty of making the turbine sufficiently watertight to avoid losing any of the valuable heavy water.

The main uncertainty about EBWR is connected with the roughness of operation caused by the boiling. As the moderator boils, its density fluctuates, and any density change will affect leakage

Experimental boiling-water reactor has the advantage of a system in which water is heated to steam by the fission process in the reactor core and passes directly into the turbine. Some of the disadvantages are the unevenness of the boiling operation in the core and the radioactivity of steam in the turbine. The fuel element will be enriched uranium.

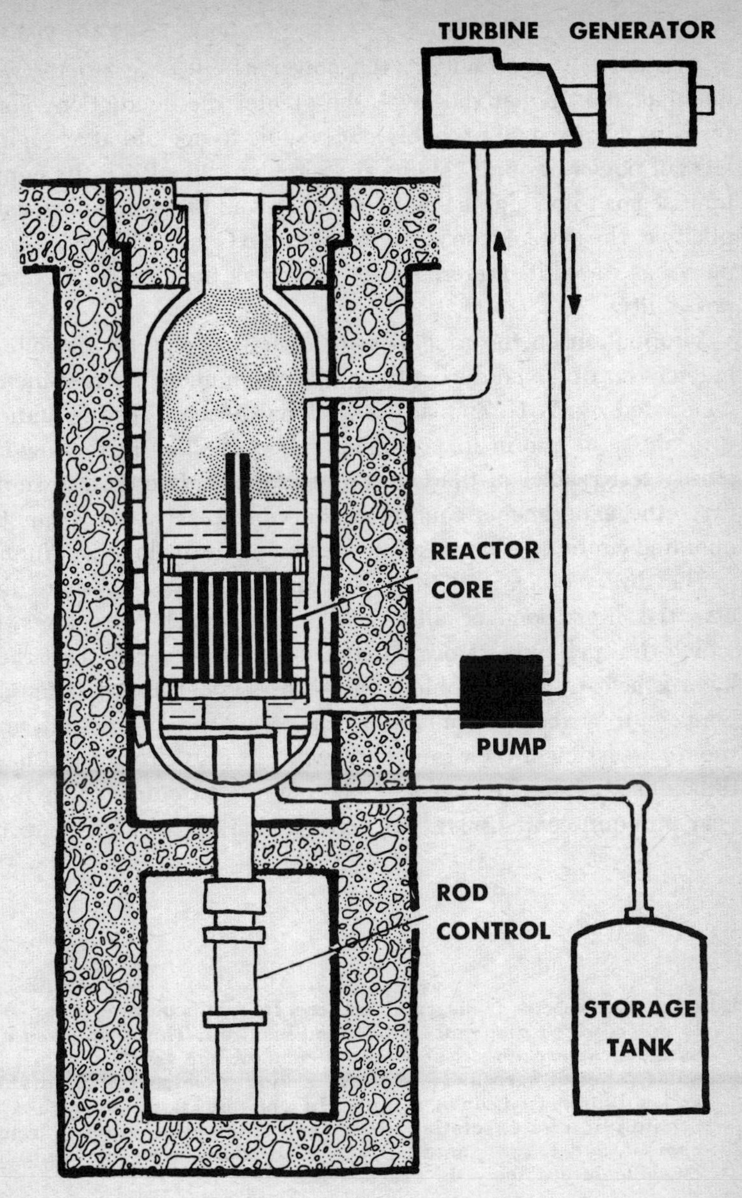
TURBINE
GENERATOR
REACTOR
CORE
PUMP
ROD
CONTROL
STORAGE
TANK

of neutrons. In consequence the power level of the reactor will fluctuate; the higher the level, the greater the fluctuation. Thus the direct boiler will probably not be able to operate at as high a level of power per unit volume as a circulator like PWR. Its upper limit seems to be high enough, however, and the mechanical simplicity of the system is so attractive that the General Electric Company has stated its preference for the direct boiler as a long-term possibility.

Information on the roughness of operation of a direct-boiling reactor was obtained during the past two summers in experiments conducted by W. H. Zinn at the National Reactor Testing Station in Idaho, and also in some experiments on boiling in the low-intensity test reactor at the Oak Ridge National Laboratory. In all cases the experiments confirmed the view that reactors can be operated continuously in a stable fashion under boiling conditions.

The direct boiler and the circulating-water system share the essential limitations of all heterogeneous reactors—reactors in which the fuel, moderator and coolant are separate. At best they have a heat-transfer problem; they are susceptible to radiation damage; they accumulate neutron-absorbing fission products, and the reprocessing of their fuel is awkward. It is to circumvent these difficulties that the homogeneous system was introduced. The five-year program contemplates the construction of two homogeneous

Homogeneous reactor is diagrammed here. Its fuel is uranium dissolved in water, which undergoes fission and heats up. This heat, given up in the heat exchanger, generates steam for the turbine. A heavy-water reflector surrounds the core. Fission products are removable and additional fuel can be injected. In a modification of this scheme, thorium in a water solution would replace the heavy-water reflector blanket, and U-233 would be bred in the thorium by the neutrons escaping into it from the reactor core.

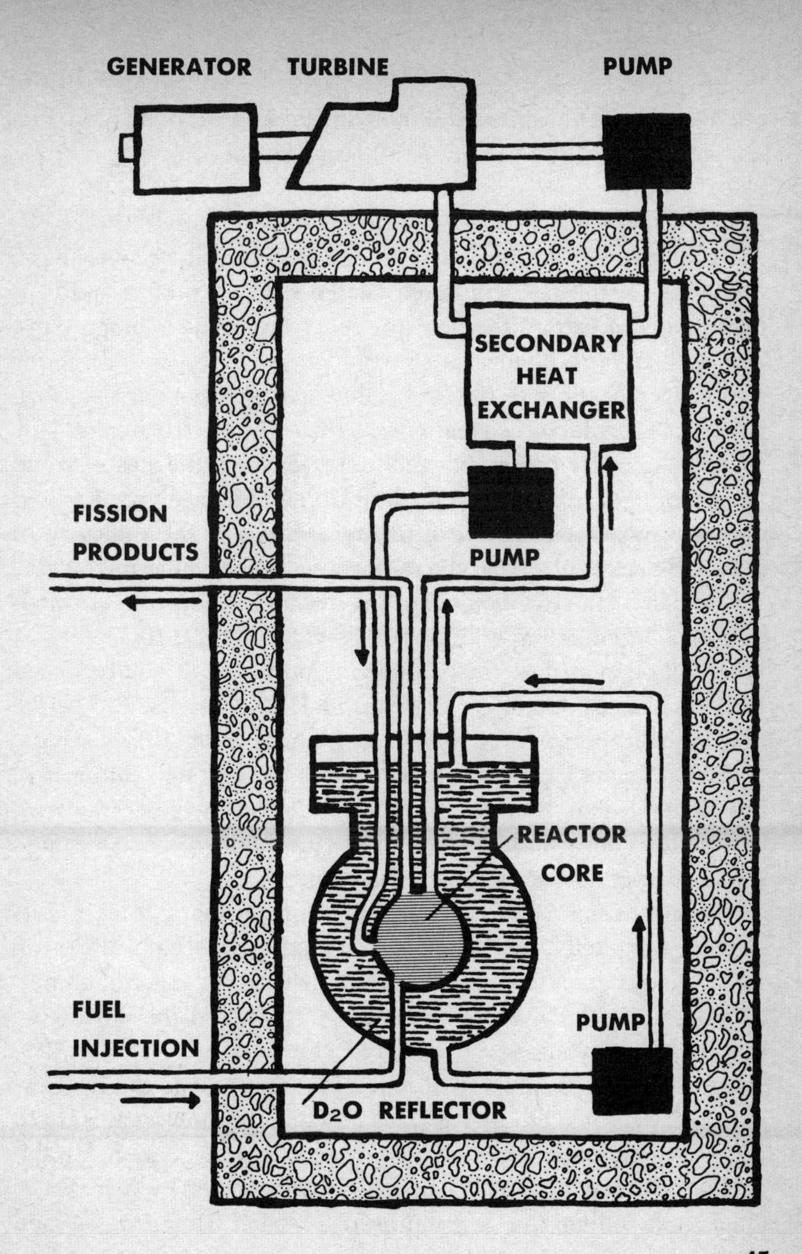
GENERATOR
TURBINE
PUMP
SECONDARY
HEAT
EXCHANGER
PUMP
FISSION
PRODUCTS
REACTOR
CORE
FUEL
INJECTION
PUMP
D_2O REFLECTOR

reactors, which constitute the third line of approach; actually it is a culmination of the two water systems described above.

In a homogeneous reactor the fuel (uranium or thorium) is dissolved in water. The uranium is in the form of a salt, uranyl sulfate. A solution of the salt will be circulated through pumps and heat exchangers to extract the heat produced by the fissioning atoms. The exchangers will generate fairly high-pressure, nonradioactive steam. It is possible to think of a direct-boiling homogeneous reactor—one in which the steam is generated in the reactor itself by boiling the water containing the fuel. However, the steam would be extremely radioactive, and the turbine that received it would be very awkward to service, to say nothing of the difficulty of making it leaktight so that the radioactive steam would not escape.

The first of the two homogeneous reactors will be a fairly modest version generating only 5,000 kilowatts of heat. Its main purpose will be to explore the engineering problems. It will be called HRE-2, because it follows the plan of HRE-1 at Oak Ridge, the first high-temperature homogeneous reactor built. It will consist of a more or less spherical vessel, in which the fuel solution will circulate through a core so shaped that the fluid will become critical and heat up; after it leaves the core the fluid will travel through piping shaped to quench any chain reaction.

The most remarkable aspect of the homogeneous reactor is its seeming simplicity. For example, there are no mechanical control rods. The system is completely self-regulating. An experiment performed on the HRE-1 dramatically demonstrated this. At a core temperature of 338 degrees F. the reactor was barely critical. The main circulating pump was stopped and the fluid in the heat exchanger was cooled to 212 degrees F. Then the pump was started. As the cooler, and therefore more reactive, fluid poured into the core of the reactor, the reactor shot up in power by a factor of almost one million in a few tenths of a second. However, as soon as the water was heated the reactor leveled off to a steady output of 1,000 kilowatts. The initial flow of cooler water into the core caused a rise of reactivity at the rate of .8 per cent per second. Such a rise in any heterogeneous reactor would almost certainly lead to fairly violent, and possibly dangerous, pressure surges.

The nuclear stability of the aqueous homogeneous system is bought at the price of having to deal with billions of curies of radioactivity in solution under high pressure; that is, one buys almost complete nuclear safety, but one pays for it with a requirement of absolute leaktightness and material control. It is to establish the engineering feasibility and long-term reliability of such a leaktight high-pressure system that HRE-2 is being built.

HRE-2 will be followed by a larger reactor with a heat output of at least 65,000 kilowatts. It is hoped that this will be the first thorium thermal breeder. This reactor (HTR) will contain thorium in heavy water, and it will manufacture U-233 in a thorium blanket.

The inherent difficulties of a homogeneous reactor, almost entirely connected with handling colossally radioactive and corrosive fluids under high pressure, are so great that the probability of success is not as high as for the more conservative types. Yet the incentive is so great that a major effort has been launched to solve the admittedly formidable engineering problems.

The remaining two reactor approaches are put together because they both will use sodium as the coolant and their external equipment will be much the same. In both reactors hot sodium from the reactors will give its heat to steam which will operate turbogenerators. In order to avoid the possibility of contact between the steam and the radioactive sodium coming from the reactor, it has usually been considered desirable to incorporate an intermediate fluid to carry the heat from the reactor sodium to the steam generator.

One of these systems is the sodium reactor experiment (SRE) designed by North American Aviation, Inc. It resembles the Hanford reactors, except that sodium replaces the water that flows past and cools the fuel elements. Its moderator will be graphite and the fuel will be disposed in tubes running through the graphite.

North American has already started construction of this 20,000-kilowatt reactor in California. From the nuclear standpoint, the reactor is conservative and so there should be no question of its ultimate success. However, there are difficult questions as to its economic outlook. Present estimates put its power cost in the range of 8 to 10 mills per kilowatt hour, which is a little high to be competitive in the U. S. Yet there are several developmental possibilities which, if successful, may ultimately lower the cost to 4 or 5 mills. These are: (1) simplification of the expensive sodium plumbing; (2) operation as a breeder or near-breeder with thorium; (3) improvement in the fuel elements to allow a higher burn-up than the one per cent suggested as the economic minimum.

A sodium-cooled reactor, which can be operated at very high temperatures, has greater thermal efficiency than a water-cooled system. Whether this advantage will overbalance the greater simplicity of the best water system is the main question to be decided.

Sodium-cooled reactor is designed around a comparatively "old-fashioned" core (like those in the Hanford piles) immersed in a cooling bath of liquid sodium. Slightly enriched uranium rods (*solid black bars*) run through channels in a graphite moderator (*hatched bars*). The liquid sodium surrounding the core circulates through a pair of cooling systems to make steam for generator. To avoid the danger of placing highly radioactive sodium near water, the coolant is made to give its heat to a second sodium loop in the primary heat exchanger. The nonradioactive fluid then boils water in the secondary heat exchanger. Concrete shields the primary units.

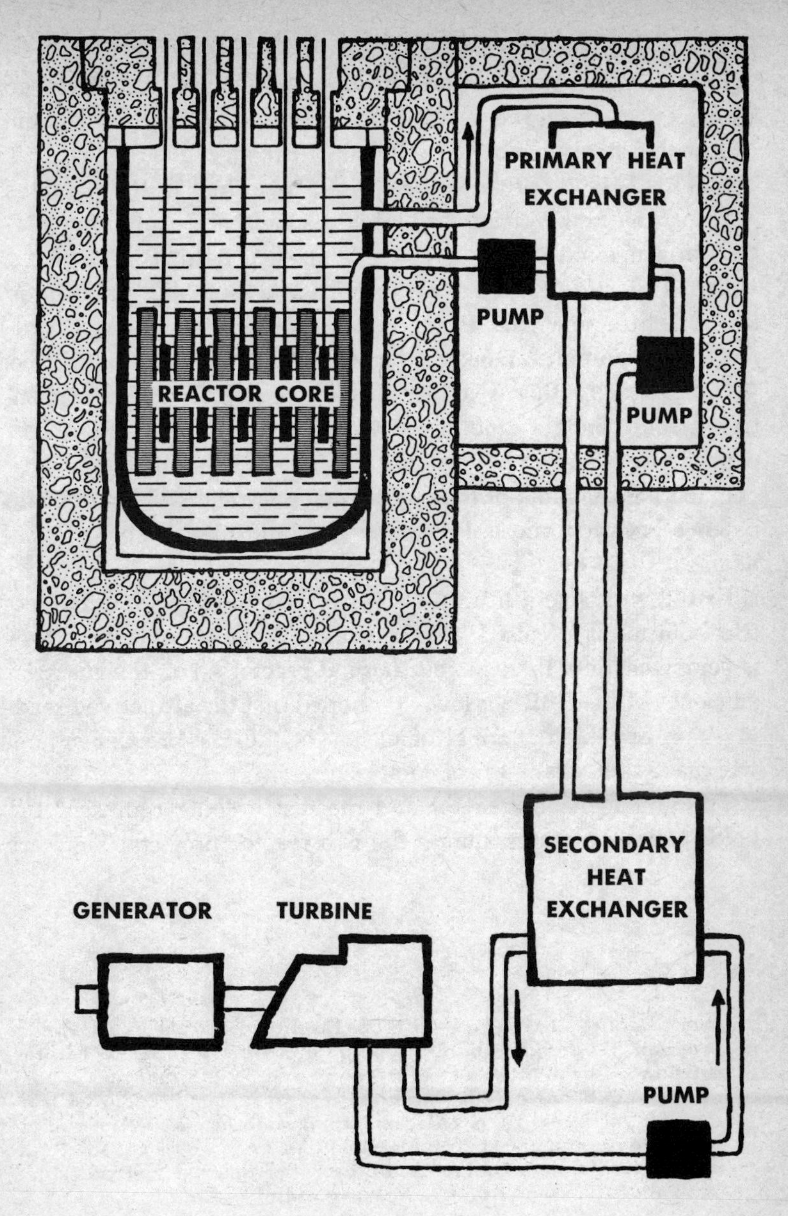
PRIMARY HEAT EXCHANGER
PUMP
REACTOR CORE
PUMP
SECONDARY HEAT EXCHANGER
GENERATOR
TURBINE
PUMP

In many ways the most advanced, and most difficult, of all the reactors in the program is the other sodium reactor—the Argonne National Laboratory's Experimental Breeder Reactor No. 2 (EBR-2). Like its predecessor EBR-1, described in the previous chapter, the new version will have a small core containing plutonium, surrounded by a breeder blanket of natural or depleted U-238. The core (EBR-1's was the size of a football) will contain no moderating material, for in order to achieve the highest breeding gain it is important to keep the neutrons as energetic as possible. In other words, this is a fast-neutron breeder. Such a concentrated fuel configuration is extremely hard to cool and is susceptible to severe radiation damage. This points up the primary engineering dilemma of the fast breeder: it must strike a delicate balance between unusable compactness and unworkable diffuseness.

EBR-2 will have a heat output of 62,500 kilowatts and an electrical output of at least 15,000 kilowatts. While the specific power is somewhat less than in the thermal reactors—i.e., the material efficiency of the EBR-2 is low—it is hoped that the attractive breeding gain and high thermal efficiency of the fast-breeder system will make the system an economic success.

The homogeneous reactor and the fast breeder represent the boldest extrapolations among the five reactor projects. They are

Experimental breeder reactor—II is the fast breeder in the experimental program. Its design calls for a plutonium core, with no moderator, surrounded by a "blanket" of natural or depleted uranium (a close-up diagram of the core is shown on page 31). Heat is removed from the compact core by circulating liquid sodium. As in the sodium reactor experiments, a secondary sodium loop serves to isolate the radioactive primary coolant from the boiler water. A concrete shield surrounds the reactor and radioactive sodium system.

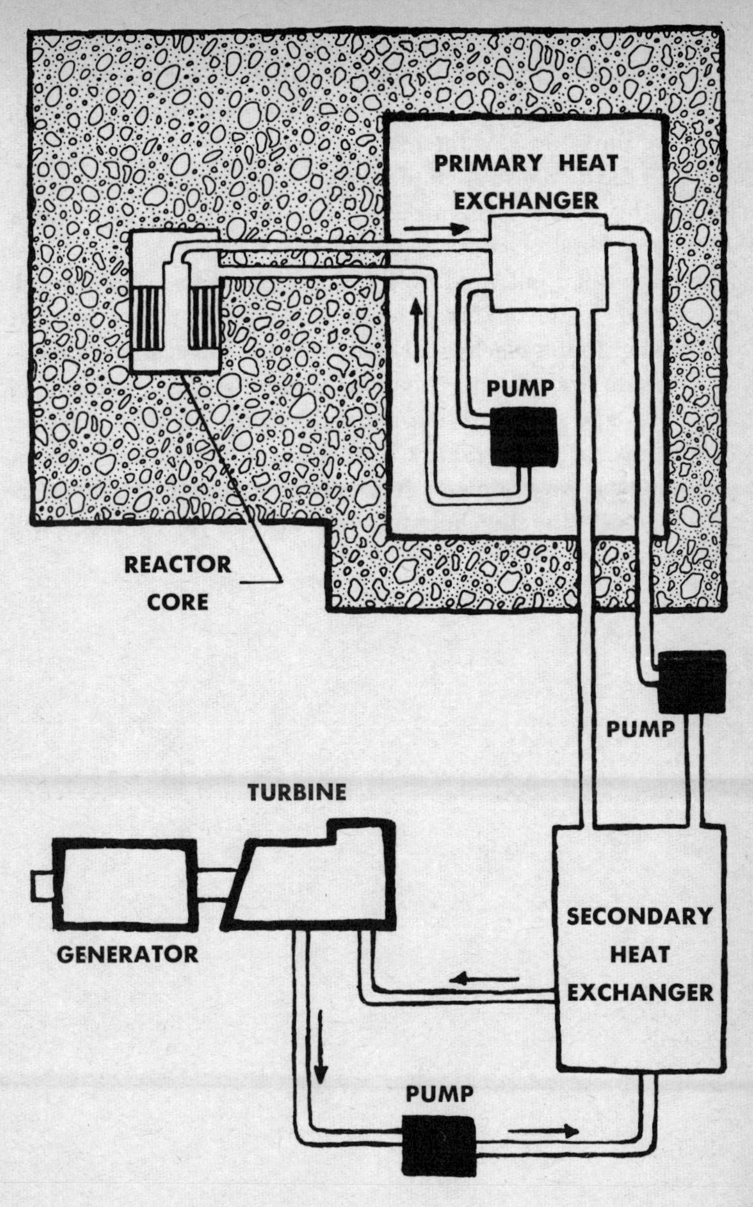
PRIMARY HEAT
EXCHANGER
PUMP
REACTOR
CORE
PUMP
TURBINE
GENERATOR
SECONDARY
HEAT
EXCHANGER
PUMP

the most difficult, but by the same token probably offer the greatest potential return. There is an essential common sense in not putting all the effort into the most advanced systems; too much is at stake in the demonstration of workable nuclear power plants to leave out the more certain but less glamorous possibilities in favor of the more glamorous but less certain reactors.

There are other potential power reactors under study or development outside the AEC's five-year program; for example, the gas-cooled graphite reactor of the British, the very attractive uranium-bismuth circulating fuel system at the Brookhaven National Laboratory, and of course the military reactors, which taken together represent a program at least as large as the program for civilian power development. It is fair to expect that five years hence the most attractive lines of nuclear power development will be clearly drawn.

THE GENEVA CONFERENCE

by Robert A. Charpie

HISTORY WILL RECORD the Geneva Conference of 1955 as the event which opened the door, for all the peoples of the earth, to the age of nuclear power. In this meeting of nuclear scientists from many countries the promise of atomic power began to take form and substance.

For uninitiated listeners the outpouring of information on power reactors at Geneva had two chief points of interest: they were interested first to hear whether nuclear power could live up to its advance press notices, and secondly to know how different countries compared in progress in this field. On the first point, they were soon satisfied that nuclear power had a very big future indeed. On the second, the listeners came away convinced that although the U. S. is still the leader in the development of advanced power reactors, other nations are rapidly closing the gap. The U.S.S.R. already has a 5,000-kilowatt electrical power plant in operation and is now building at least one larger version of the same reactor type which will generate 100,000 kilowatts of electricity. Great Britain will have the first large-scale reactor plant operating at Calder Hall by the end of 1956. It will supply power to the British Electric Authority grid. The first large U. S. power station—the 60,000-kilowatt plant being built by Westinghouse near Pittsburgh—will not begin operating until 1958, but the Geneva reports on the broad, diverse program being pursued in the U. S. left no doubt that the nuclear-power effort of this nation is the most advanced in the world.

The scientists representing nations not yet committed to nuclear energy found the conference a revelation. For the first time all the pertinent technical facts were publicly available. Even cynical observers had to agree that the conference had furnished enough information to permit any nation to decide whether it wished to go into the nuclear power business and how best to begin.

Some of the most significant facts that might influence these decisions were presented in the reactor physics sessions dealing with the fundamental properties of fissionable materials. The main focus of interest was the "breeding" question: What are the prospects for realizing practicable power reactors which will breed more fuel than they consume?

The only naturally occurring fissionable material that can serve as fuel for a reactor is uranium 235. Unfortunately U-235 makes up only 71 hundredths of 1 per cent of natural uranium. But the idea that the more plentiful U-238 could be burned by converting it into fissionable plutonium in a "breeder reactor" has been in the minds of reactor physicists ever since plutonium was discovered more than 12 years ago. In theory the possibilities are perfectly simple. All one needs is a supply of neutrons sufficient to continue the chain reaction in the reactor and also to manufacture plutonium from U-238. Plutonium itself is the best source of neutrons, for when a plutonium atom captures a high-energy neutron and fissions, its fission yields, on the average, about 2.9 neutrons—a

Russian power reactor employs pressurized water system. It furnishes energy for the 5,000-kilowatt atomic power station of the U.S.S.R. Academy of Sciences. Heat of fission in its lattice of uranium rods and graphite is absorbed by circulating distilled water, which is kept under a pressure of 1,500 pounds per square inch. Pressure raises the boiling point of water and enables it to absorb more heat. The heat exchanger reduces the temperature of the water from about 270 to 190 degrees Centigrade, thereby extracting the energy for generating electric power. The Russians announced at Geneva that they plan to construct a 100,000-kilowatt version of this reactor.

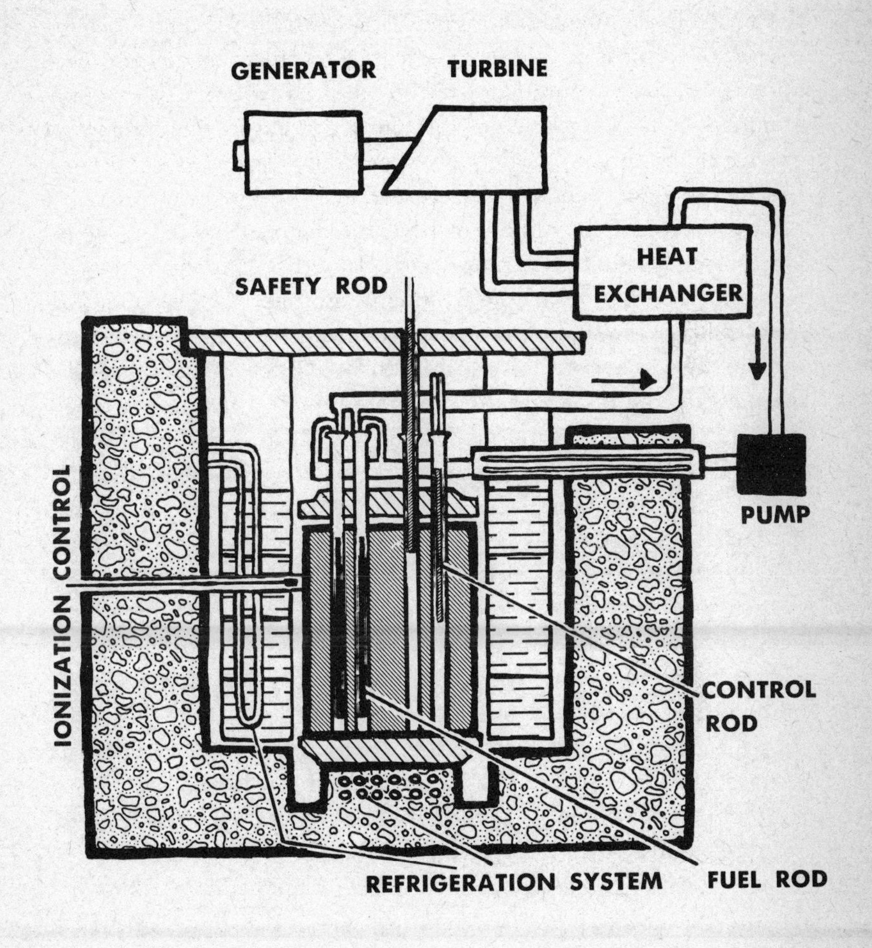
GENERATOR
TURBINE
HEAT EXCHANGER
SAFETY ROD
IONIZATION CONTROL
PUMP
CONTROL ROD
REFRIGERATION SYSTEM
FUEL ROD

better yield than from the fission of U-235. In a reactor utilizing plutonium fuel (which of course must first be made from U-238 with neutrons from an initial charge of fissioning U-235), one of the neutrons from each plutonium fission would sustain the chain reaction and most of the remainder (1.9 on the average) presumably could be captured by U-238 to produce new plutonium atoms. Since the number of plutonium atoms manufactured is greater than the number destroyed, as time goes on the amount of fuel in a breeder reactor will increase.

Likewise thorium could be the basis of a similar breeding cycle. When a thorium atom captures a neutron, the reaction results in formation of an atom of the fissionable isotope uranium 233, just as U-238 is converted by neutron capture into fissionable plutonium. The conversion of thorium to U-233 does not require fast neutrons, as the manufacture of plutonium does. It can be carried out with low-energy (thermal) neutrons. This considerably simplifies the problems in designing the reactor. However, there is also a debit side: in the U-233 cycle the neutron economy is tighter, for U-233 releases only 2.3 neutrons instead of 2.9.

In these breeding schemes it is a long step from theory to practice, because there are so many elements in a reactor which tend to rob the cycle of its neutron supply. Until Geneva every country's experiments in breeding were classified, so that the practical feasibility of the idea was wrapped in mystery. But when the delegates brought their data out from under wraps and compared notes at Geneva, it became plain that enough has been learned to assure that both the uranium and the thorium breeding cycles will work.

The British reported the results of breeding experiments with their Zero Energy Fast Reactor (ZEPHYR). This is a laboratory reactor operating at low temperature without cooling. ZEPHYR is uncomplicated by the structural materials and coolant that a power reactor would require; nonetheless it achieves breeding by a large enough margin (about two for one) to demonstrate that a reactor with the additional structure needed for generating power would still be a breeder.

The U. S. described its successful experiments in breeding with a reactor which is an actual prototype of a power unit. The Experimental Breeder Reactor (EBR) at the Idaho Testing Station, whose achievement of breeding was first announced in December 1953, has a liquid metal coolant (sodium) and a uranium breeding blanket.

In the case of thorium, elaborate experiments to demonstrate the feasibility of breeding are less necessary. The fundamental nuclear constants are now known sufficiently to calculate the neutron economy of this cycle quite accurately. France, the U.S.S.R., Great Britain and the U. S. all contributed information on the pertinent reactions, and the Oak Ridge National Laboratory reported some direct experimental measurements of the critical mass required for a U-233 chain reaction. The critical mass is about 20 kilograms of U-233 for a slow-neutron reactor. Taking all the data together, it is possible to predict reliably that a power reactor can be built which will operate as a U-233 breeder.

One of the most interesting developments of the conference was the comparison of critical cross-section measurements by groups of scientists in various countries. These measurements have been closely guarded secrets. It was therefore something of a surprise to discover at Geneva that the measurements in all countries, carried out independently, agreed almost exactly! Rarely has there been such a classic demonstration of the principle that "truth will out," despite all attempts to hide it.

In nuclear physics "cross section" is the measure of the statistical probability that a specified nuclear event will occur. For instance, when a physicist speaks of the absorption, or capture, cross section of U-238 for slow neutrons, he means the likelihood of capture under the given conditions; the fission cross section similarly is the probability for occurrence of fission. The cross section is expressed as an area, and the unit area (10^{-24} square centimeters) was almost immediately named a "barn"—by analogy with the proverbial barn door, though an area like 10^{-24} square centimeters is of course an extremely small unit.

At Geneva representatives of the leading countries in nuclear research adopted a set of average values for cross sections of the three fissionable materials for thermal neutrons, defined as having a speed of 2,200 meters per second. These standards, taking account of the margins of error and the spread of the different measurements, are as follows: The capture cross section of U-235 is 698 ± 10 barns and its fission cross section is 590 ± 15 barns; for plutonium the respective figures are $1{,}032 \pm 15$ and 729 ± 15 barns; for U-233 they are 593 ± 8 and 524 ± 8 barns.

There are still significant gaps in our knowledge of the nuclear constants important to reactor design. Any country entering the field of nuclear energy will therefore have to make certain fundamental measurements to design the types of reactor its scientists may decide upon. The most powerful tool for neutron research of this kind is, of course, a research reactor. Since a research reactor can be used simultaneously for the production of radioisotopes and for the testing of materials and reactor components, it is only natural that there was keen interest exhibited on all sides in the sessions dealing with research reactors.

A very noticeable change has taken place in the entire research reactor business during the past year. Reactors using enriched fuel and providing a high neutron flux have replaced natural-uranium reactors for research. The reason is that they greatly speed up the measurements and other studies. The British have several enriched-fuel research reactors under construction, and one of the surprises of the conference was the discovery that the Russians have several already operating. Such reactors will become available to any country through the international pool and the bilateral agreements whereby the U. S. has agreed to supply uranium enriched to 20 per cent.

Geneva provided information on two other factors important in power-reactor technology: safety and power-cost estimates.

The bogeyman of the infant industry is the specter of what might happen if a power reactor should get out of control and spread radioactive fission products over a large area. Although reactors are designed so that there is a built-in tendency to overcome runaways automatically, accidents are always possible. To see what might happen in such an accident, the U. S. performed experiments in which water-cooled reactors were deliberately allowed to run away—the so-called Borax experiments. The tests established that it is much more difficult to arrange a destructive blowup than had previously been imagined. And the runaway reactor spread its radioactive fuel and fission products only over a small area around the site. A system utilizing heavy water would be even safer than the ordinary-water reactors destroyed in the Borax experiments. Consequently it appears that it would be safe to build power reactors near large centers of population.

In the realm of reactor economics there is a growing optimism springing from the fact that improvements in the technology have made it possible to construct reactors which were formerly only figments of engineering imagination. Predictions on capital costs nowadays are based on actual bids, not on guesses. And operating costs can be predicted from experience with experimental reactors already in being.

To summarize the state of the technology it is convenient to classify the reactor systems according to the coolant employed: gas, water or liquid metal.

The primary exponents of gas-cooled power reactors are the British. Their first power station at Calder Hall will use as the coolant carbon dioxide, which has relatively good heat-transfer properties and possesses the advantage of being chemically inert. Sir Christopher Hinton described this type of reactor as "the slow-speed reciprocating engine of the reactor world." It is necessarily large; it is reliable, and its design and operating characteristics permit the use of conventional materials and techniques of construction. While the first plant will produce electricity at the exorbitant cost of nine mills per kilowatt hour (against seven mills from coal in England), it seems certain that operating experience will lower the cost in later versions. But gas-cooled reactors, even in a high-power-cost country like Great Britain, do not seem to have an unlimited future.

The British propose at least two more gas-cooled reactors in their plan for the next 10 years. Research is continuing along three major directions in an effort to make significant improvements over the Calder Hall design. In the first place, consideration is being given to replacing the carbon dioxide coolant. Helium is an ideal cooling gas, because it has a high specific heat and does not capture neutrons, but it is very expensive and is not available in large quantities in Great Britain. Another possibility is hydrogen, which has remarkable heat-transfer and moderating properties, but at high temperatures it would affect the mechanical properties of the fuel and reactor materials. A second improvement being considered by the British is the use of slightly enriched uranium as fuel

British power reactor, employing gas as the heat transfer medium, built at Calder Hall. It is described as "the slow-speed reciprocating engineer of the reactor world." It is bulky but reliable and relatively simple to construct. Helium, which is chemically inert and does not absorb neutrons, would be the ideal coolant, but it is too expensive in Britain. Carbon dioxide is the initial coolant; a better one may be found. The core is a lattice of graphite and uranium, possibly enriched. A chimney vents air pumped through to cool the reactor shielding.

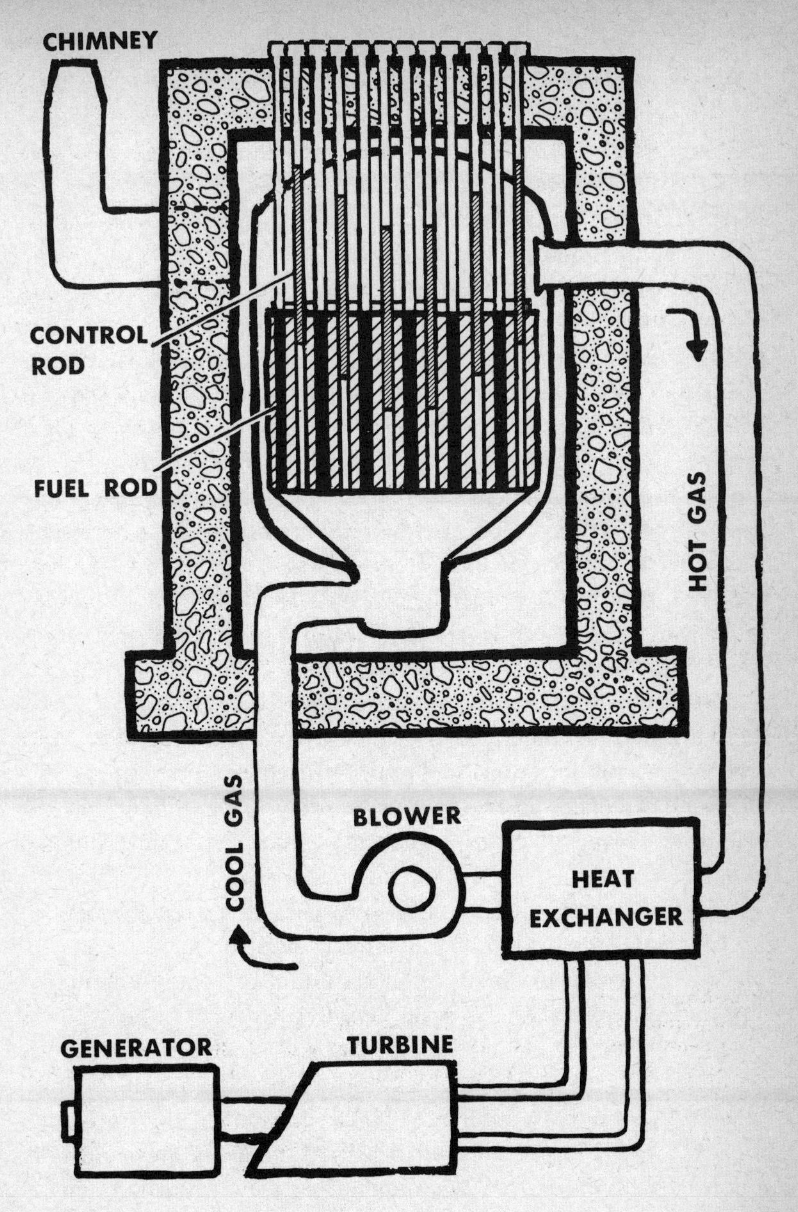
CHIMNEY
CONTROL ROD
FUEL ROD
HOT GAS
COOL GAS
BLOWER
HEAT EXCHANGER
GENERATOR
TURBINE

in the periphery of the reactor. This would have the effect of making the neutron flux and the generation of heat more nearly uniform across the whole reactor and thus increase the electrical output of the reactor. Finally, the British expect to improve the design, fabrication and performance of individual components such as blowers and heat exchangers.

Realizing that the gas-cooled reactor has limitations as a competitor in the power field, the British are also working on other types, such as the fast breeder and the homogeneous thermal breeder. Nevertheless Hinton stated quite unequivocally that the Calder Hall reactors will continue to occupy an important place in the field of reactor power for many years to come.

The water-cooled reactors form a large family. Pressurized water reactors, cooled and moderated by either ordinary or heavy water, are under development in virtually every country now involved in atomic energy. The range of concepts runs the gamut from the natural-uranium-heavy-water type under development in Canada to a homogeneous thorium breeder being developed at the Oak Ridge National Laboratory. Between these two extremes in water-cooled design fall the Pittsburgh pressurized water reactor, using slightly enriched uranium fuel and light water as the moderator; the Russian version of the same type now in operation, and the boiling-water reactor being constructed by the Argonne National Laboratory.

Water is attractive because of its low cost, its excellent moderating properties, its well-known chemistry and the large amount of engineering experience in using water under extremes of temperature and pressure that has been acquired in conventional power plants.

The Soviet power station is a pressurized water reactor moderated with graphite. In order to obtain operation at sufficiently high temperatures to procure power the fuel elements are canned in stainless steel instead of aluminum. The steel absorbs so many

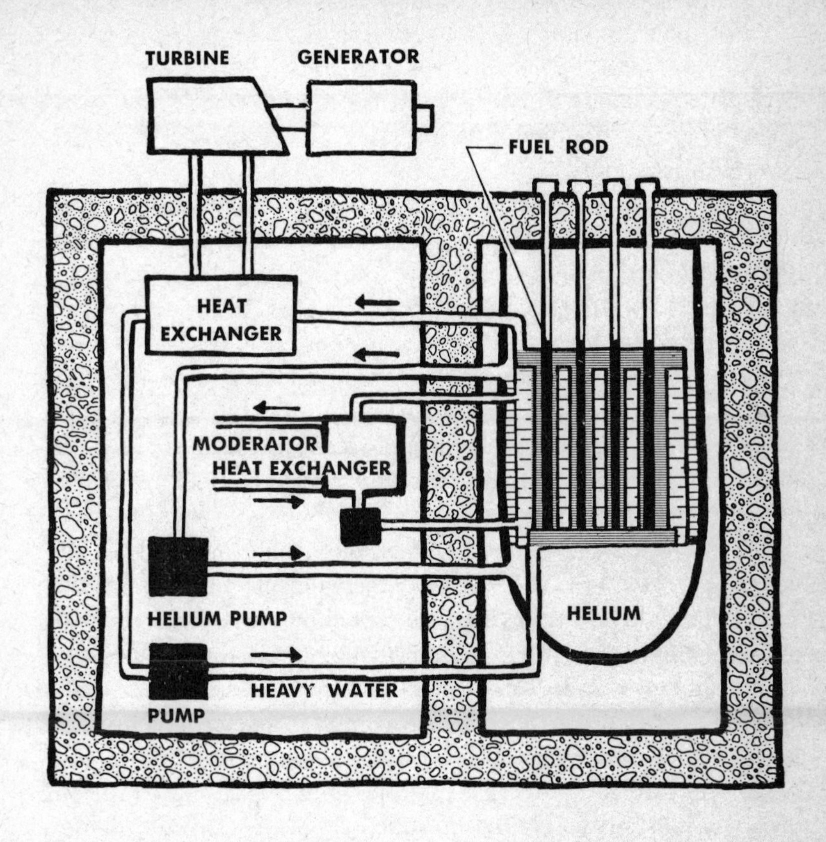

Canadian power reactor is designed on a pressurized heavy-water circuit. When completed in 1958 at Des Joachims, Ontario, it will generate 10,000 to 20,000 kilowatts of electricity. Heavy water is chosen because it absorbs almost no neutrons. In this reactor it plays two roles: coolant and neutron moderator. Small circuit at left of core keeps temperature of moderator within bounds. Larger circuits transfer energy from heated heavy water to light water, which turns to steam and drives turbines. Helium circuit is a novel safety feature. When the gas pressure is shut off, the moderator drains into bulge beneath core, and fission ceases.

neutrons that it is necessary to use enriched uranium (10 per cent U-235) as the fuel. Soviet engineers stated that the reactor produces electricity at a cost which compares favorably with coal-fueled plants of the same rating. The Soviet Union is now going ahead with the design and construction of at least one larger version of this station.

Research and development on the two most advanced water-cooled designs—the boiling-water and aqueous homogeneous reactors—are proceeding very satisfactorily indeed in the U. S. Power-plant prototypes of both reactor systems are now under construction. It appears that either of these reactors can produce power at costs competitive with coal or oil stations in the U. S. The long-range prospects of the homogeneous type reactor seem slightly better, but the technology is less advanced at this time. (The Russians presented a paper on the design of a boiling version of the homogeneous reactor.)

R. B. Briggs and J. A. Swartout of Oak Ridge reported the discovery of a simple and effective processing scheme for removing both the manufactured fissionable fuel and a large fraction of the long-lived fission products from a homogeneous thermal breeder. This would not only be a great step forward in efficiency but would also offer for the first time the prospect of a reactor which would not dangerously contaminate the environs in the event of an accident. The Oak Ridge workers also pointed out that the aqueous homogeneous reactor is the most strongly self-stabilizing design known.

Among the reactors of the class cooled with liquid metal two interesting systems were presented in detail for the first time at Geneva. One was the North American Aviation design, which employs graphite as the moderator and liquid sodium as the coolant. A molten metal not only has much better capacities for heat transfer than water but also by-passes problems which grow out of the requirement for very high pressures in a water-cooled reactor. The sodium-cooled graphite system has the advantage of high flexibility. That such a reactor can be built is now assured. As proposed by its designers, the North American Aviation reactor can operate as a converter to make power and either plutonium or U-233.

The other liquid-metal reactor described at Geneva was the fast breeder. This is the most advanced design of all. The U. S. and Great Britain have embarked on the development of fast breeder reactors, but to date only the U. S. has built and operated an engineering experiment which actually made both fissionable material and power.

Many design and operating problems must be solved, however, before the fast breeder can seriously be considered as a reasonable commercial enterprise on which to risk capital. In the first place, the fast reactor is not strongly self-regulating. This fact, coupled with the very rapid generation of neutrons, makes it necessary to take more precautions with the control and safety system. Secondly, there is the abiding paradox that in order to maximize the power potential it is desirable to have as high a proportion of "fertile" material (U-238) as possible, while on the other hand too much dilution of the fissionable fuel (plutonium) reduces the breeding performance of the system. Thirdly, irradiation damages the fuel, changing its mechanical and heat-transfer properties. Since fuel preparation is an expensive business, there is considerable incentive to keep the fuel in the reactor for as long a period as possible. Thus a difficult operational compromise must be reached: fission products must be removed from the fuel as often as practicable but not so often that it becomes too expensive.

Walter Zinn of Argonne, who is in charge of the project, indicated that despite the difficulties a large-scale fast reactor will be built in the not too distant future.

The upshot of the Geneva Conference was a great strengthening of the incentive for nuclear-power development throughout the world. The conference made clear that while nuclear energy is surely not a panacea for all the troubles of the world, it can help to solve the problems of the power-starved and underdeveloped countries. The diligent search for the best methods of harnessing nuclear power on a large scale will go on at an ever-increasing pace in every country, and the age of nuclear power should certainly arrive within the next 10 years.

PART 2 RESOURCES

I. THE EARTH'S URANIUM
by Paul F. Kerr

A Californian by birth, Paul F. Kerr is professor of geology at Columbia University. He graduated from Occidental College in Los Angeles in 1919 and got his Ph.D. at Stanford University in 1923. Kerr has been on the Columbia faculty since 1924 and has been a consultant to the federal government atomic energy enterprise on its resources problems since 1944.

II. URANIUM FROM COAL
by Ralph L. Miller and James R. Gill

The authors are on the staff of the U. S. Geological Survey. Ralph L. Miller took his Ph.D. in geology at Columbia University in 1937. He joined the Geological Survey full time in 1942 and is now chief of the Survey's Fuels Branch. His original interest in coal goes back to his early years in his native Pennsylvania. James R. Gill went into geology after several years as a combat aerial photographer in World War II, during which he received the Air Medal and two Oak Leaf Clusters.

THE EARTH'S URANIUM

by Paul F. Kerr

THE MOST IMPORTANT sources of uranium in the world are the Shinkolobwe mine in the Belgian Congo, two mines in northwest Canada, the Erz Mountains on the boundary between Czechoslovakia and East Germany and the Colorado Plateau in the U. S. Not long ago the latter area was not considered in the same class with the first three. But intensive prospecting and new geological knowledge have greatly increased our known resources. Today the U. S. production of uranium is an important factor in the world supply.

Uranium is a fairly common element, present almost everywhere in the earth's crust. The problem is to find it in concentrations that make it worth while to try to mine it. It has been suggested that we could get 70 tons of uranium from every cubic mile of sea water. This sounds impressive until one makes a simple calculation and finds that a cubic mile of sea water weighs about four billion tons—70 tons of uranium in that bulk of "ore" amounts to about one part in 60 million. There are many rock masses in the earth with a uranium content of one part in 10,000, but even this concentration is considered much too thin for mining by present methods. To interest mining engineers a deposit must have a uranium content of at least one part in a few hundred; that is, at least several pounds of uranium per ton of ore.

There are more than 80 known minerals that contain substantial amounts of uranium, but less than a dozen are at all abundant in the earth. The richest mineral is uraninite, a combination of uranium dioxide (UO_2) and trioxide (UO_3). This exists in black powdery and solid crystalline forms. Pitchblende is a variety of uraninite. Usually uraninite occurs in relatively deep deposits. The other important uranium minerals ordinarily are found near the earth surface. They are carnotite, a canary-yellow powder in which uranium is combined with potassium and vanadium; torbernite, a green crystal phosphate of uranium and copper; autunite, a yellow crystal phosphate of uranium and calcium; tyuyamunite, a yellow powder containing uranium, calcium and vanadium; thucholite, a black organic material in which uranium is combined with a hydrocarbon; and kolm, another uranium-hydrocarbon combination.

Carnotite is the most common uranium mineral in the Colorado Plateau. Torbernite is found in large masses near the surface in the Belgian Congo, where the richest deposits of uraninite are located. Good deposits of autunite are found in Portugal. Tyuyamunite is named for a city in a region of the U.S.S.R. where it is particularly abundant.

In looking around the world for likely sources of uranium minerals the geologist has certain general principles to guide him. He will look, of course, to faults, fissures and pockets in the earth's crust, where minerals in general are concentrated, and he will search for chemical and physical conditions that particularly favor the precipitation of uranium. He knows that concentrations of uranium often occur in veins cutting the granitic igneous rocks. Uranium (with its companion radium) tends to be associated in veins with certain other minerals, notably cobalt, nickel, bismuth and a few others, including small amounts of silver and gold. During the recent worldwide hunt for uranium another apparently significant fact has emerged: many of the uranium deposits have been found in ancient Pre-Cambrian rocks. It is believed to be more than a coincidence that the chief uranium locations in the Belgian Congo, the Erz Mountains, Canada, eastern Colorado and at several other places are all in Pre-Cambrian formations.

We can see the uranium picture most conveniently by reviewing briefly the history of each of the principal locations.

The town of Joachimsthal in the Erz Mountains has been a mining center since the fifteenth century. For centuries the only metal mined was silver. The American word "dollar" is derived from the name of silver coins struck there, first called *Joachimsthaler* and later abbreviated to *thaler*. In the middle of the nineteenth century the element uranium was discovered in the Joachimsthal ores, but the only use then found for it was as a pigment for porcelain and glass. When in 1898 the Curies isolated radium, a product of the radioactive decay of uranium, from the uranium residues of Joachimsthal, the mines rose in importance; for many years they were the world's sole source of radium. Up to World War II they had yielded a total of 100 grams of radium.

The uranium-bearing formations of the Erz Mountains lie along two mountain belts which intersect at Joachimsthal. The mountains, once the boundary between Saxony and Bohemia, now are on the border between the Russian zone of Germany and Czechoslovakia. The principal uranium mineral in these deposits is uraninite. It lies in veins ranging from less than an inch to several feet in thickness. The veins also contain minerals of silver, cobalt, nickel and bismuth. They represent old fissures in the earth's crust that were partly filled by the precipitation of metallic minerals from ascending solutions. The wall rock consists of recrystallized sediments of Pre-Cambrian age.

Uranium is reported as U_3O_8. The total amount of U_3O_8 mined in the Erz Gebirge region up to 1940 is estimated at 690 tons. We can only guess at how much the Russians may have obtained from their intensive mining of the area since the end of the war. In all likelihood the amount is at least several hundred tons.

To estimate the total extent of the uranium resources available to the U.S.S.R. we must extrapolate from what was known about them before 1944, for little information has been revealed from behind the Iron Curtain since that time. The principal uranium deposits in the U.S.S.R. before 1944 were considered to lie in the black shales and slates of the desert area of Asiatic Russia between Lake Balkhash and the Afghanistan border. This is the region where the mineral known as tyuyamunite is found. The Alai Range in the same general area also is reported to possess large amounts of black shales or slates containing on the order of a pound of uranium per ton of rock, but the labor required to work these deposits would be great indeed. Near-surface deposits of a uranium mineral are known to exist in Bulgaria. In addition the U.S.S.R. was known to possess scattered deposits of uranium minerals such as occur in other parts of the world; probably these are numerous enough to yield significant quantities of fissionable material.

According to press accounts some 3,000 geologists are exploring for uranium in the U.S.S.R. It must be assumed that they have made considerable progress. Whether the state-operated Soviet effort will ultimately produce more and cheaper uranium than will the co-operative efforts of government and private industry in the U. S., time alone will tell. But if any credence may be placed in the newspaper reports that hundreds of thousands of Russian workers are engaged in mining and hunting uranium, with digging and prospecting going on in 230 locations in eastern Germany alone, we may well conclude that the present uranium production available to the U.S.S.R. is seriously large.

Our first source of supply is the Shinkolobwe mine in the Belgian Congo. Shinkolobwe is in the heart of Africa, about midway between the continent's east and west coasts and near the southern margin of the Congo Basin about 11 degrees south of the Equator. It lies in the center of a great mineral province long famous for its production of copper, cobalt, tin and diamonds; the province produces most of the world's industrial diamonds and leads the world in the production of cobalt.

In 1915 a Major Sharp, prospecting for minerals as an employee of the Tanganyika Concession, noticed some unusual bright yellow fragments of rock in the soil at Shinkolobwe. Analysis showed that they were rich in uranium. The concessionaires dug trenches and soon exposed veins of black uraninite. Later explorations disclosed masses of rock containing the highest percentages of uranium found anywhere. Near the surface above these veins lie brightly colored uranium minerals—yellow, orange or green—some of which have been found nowhere else in the world.

The Shinkolobwe area is one in which Pre-Cambrian rocks of varying ages are exposed at the surface. Curiously, in some places an older Pre-Cambrian rock lies on top of a younger; the layers apparently were overturned by faulting and deformation of the crust. It is in the older rock that the most important uranium deposits have been found. How the uraninite was deposited in this rock is a matter of conjecture. Originally the uranium came from deep in the earth crust. It rose in heated solutions and was deposited in spaces in the shattered rock of the old Pre-Cambrian strata as uraninite. The deformation that thrust the old layer upward then raised the veins of uraninite close to the surface. Some such explanation seems necessary to account for the emergence of so rich a concentration of uranium at Shinkolobwe—unmatched, as far as we know, anywhere else on the surface of the earth.

The uranium deposits of Canada are in another great area of exposed Pre-Cambrian rocks, but in this case the ancient rocks have been laid bare by erosion of the younger rocks that covered them. Anyone who flies over the Canadian Shield can hardly fail to be impressed by the great number of scattered lakes, seemingly always extending to the horizon. The land areas between the lakes have been so swept by the great ice sheet which once covered the entire area that when viewed from the air they appear to have been planed. The surface is furrowed, however, with a network of fault lines that show up in the topography as long narrow depressions filled with trees, bushes and muskeg. It is along such fault lines or other fractures parallel to them that the Canadian uranium deposits were found and much of the uranium prospecting in the northland has been carried on of late.

The original Eldorado deposit was discovered in 1930 by the Canadian prospector Gilbert LaBine. On the east shore of Great Bear Lake, in a wilderness only a short distance south of the Arctic Circle, he spotted from the air a vein which proved to contain uraninite. It was later traced for several thousand feet and found to belong to a group of five neighboring veins. The original vein, named "No. 1," in places is as much as 30 feet thick.

Intensive mining began during the war, when the need for uranium for the Manhattan Project developed. Since the Eldorado mine is 1,380 miles by boat and 800 miles by air from the nearest railhead in the province of Alberta, transportation is a problem. The uranium oxide is shipped to the railhead over a circuitous route by way of several lakes and rivers. The Eldorado Mining and Refining Company, Ltd., operator of the mine, also runs its own airline from Eldorado to Edmonton. The company is controlled by the Canadian Government.

Since the end of the war the great Canadian Shield has been extensively prospected. Uranium has been found at various places in a zone which extends from Great Bear Lake southward through Great Slave Lake and Lake Athabaska and finally eastward along the northern shore of Lake Superior. Near the eastern arm of Lake Athabaska the Eldorado Company has recently found a group of veins along what is known as the St. Louis fault. On the basis of extensive drilling and tunneling into the shattered rock the engineers have concluded that this deposit will yield an amount of uranium comparable to that from the Eldorado site. It is expected to begin producing before the end of this year.

In the U. S. the main center of prospecting has been the Colorado Plateau, which covers parts of the four states of Colorado, Utah, Arizona and New Mexico. The ore here, as we have noted, is carnotite, a vanadate of potassium and uranium. It occurs in old sandstones formed in what seems once to have been a shallow freshwater sea. The sandstone contains a great many fossil logs and other plant remains. In some of the logs carnotite has replaced part of the original material. One such log, 4 feet thick and 100 feet long, yielded 105 tons of uranium-vanadium-radium ore. The market value of this log at the time it was mined is reported to have been about $230,000.

The logs and other vegetable matter appear to have been important factors in the accumulation of the concentrations of uranium and vanadium. Presumably the organic matter played a part in the chemical reduction and precipitation from solutions of dissolved salts containing uranium.

Deposits of carnotite underlie large areas in Colorado, Utah, Arizona and New Mexico. The U. S. sources of uranium are not restricted to carnotite. Near Marysvale, Utah, significant veins of uraninite have been found. Another encouraging discovery of uranium ore has recently been made at the old Sunshine silver mine in the Coeur d'Alene district of Idaho. There are also promising veins bearing uranium in the granitic rocks of western Montana. The Pre-Cambrian formations of the northern Michigan Peninsula have shown possibilities, but no workable deposits as yet.

Throughout much of the western U. S. an army of prospectors is searching for uranium with an enthusiasm that must be witnessed to be appreciated. The "uranium rush" is producing new types of prospectors. Radio technicians, businessmen and people of many other occupations who have never had any interest in mining have equipped themselves with Geiger counters and assailed the hills in search of radioactive rocks. They have reported many usable prospects, and some of these are already being mined. One interesting deposit was discovered accidentally by a plumber on a picnic. He was amusing himself with a portable Geiger counter and happened on some loose rocks that showed unusual radioactivity. He then traced the rocks to the uranium deposit. An attractive feature of uranium-hunting is that it can be carried on with little more equipment than a Geiger counter; anyone can be a prospector, even if he does not know much about rocks. And a search of the terrain with a Geiger counter is a fascinating experience.

It appears that it may also become possible to explore for uranium from the air. The U. S. Geological Survey, working with the Atomic Energy Commission, has made tests of this possibility with low-flying planes carrying specially built counters. Some planes fly slowly over the terrain at an altitude of about 500 feet. They have been able to locate rock deposits of unusual radioactivity within about a quarter of a mile. Such a survey is very crude, of course, and it must be followed up with a more intensive exploration on the ground, which may eventually come to naught. But the survey can cover a great deal of terrain in a relatively short time.

From the finds of the prospectors and from geological studies we are steadily enlarging our knowledge of the occurrence of uranium in the earth. The deposits found are being scrutinized by geologists; the minerals taken from them are being studied in the laboratory. These analyses provide further clues as to the types of formations where uranium is likely to exist. The studies are not restricted to high-grade sources of the metal. Recently attention has been directed to the fact, previously overlooked, that the gold ores of the Witwatersrand in South Africa contain some uranium. The average uranium content of these rocks is small, but with 60 million tons of gold ore passing through the Witwatersrand mills each year, the salvage of even a small amount of uranium from each ton may well be worth while. In our own country there are known to be large deposits of uranium-bearing phosphate rock in Florida, Idaho and western Wyoming, black shale in Tennessee and pegmatites scattered through many parts of the nation. These ores are of very low grade—one pound of uranium in several tons of rock—but in the aggregate they constitute an enormous potential reserve.

As our information accumulates, it appears more and more evident that uranium is deposited in the earth in much the same way and by much the same processes as other metals, such as copper, lead, silver, cobalt and nickel. In fact, uranium is often associated with those metals, as we have seen. Hence we should increasingly be able to apply our long-established knowledge of the older minerals to the newer problem of uranium prospecting. Given unrestricted peacetime publication of geological information, and the incentive of industrial demand, man should learn a great deal more about the earth's uranium resources.

URANIUM FROM COAL

by Ralph L. Miller and James R. Gill

North of the Black Hills in the Dakotas is a desolate region furrowed here and there with "badlands"—mazes of gullies and small canyons. Except in particularly wet years the countryside is largely barren of vegetation. Most of the landscape is nearly flat, but its general monotony is broken in places by buttes standing 300 to 600 feet above the plain. They range in size from small knobs to mesas several miles long and a mile wide. The more prominent ones bear colorful names such as Slim Buttes, Table Mountain, Medicine Pole Hills, Cave Hills, Bullion Butte and Sentinel Butte. These buttes have recently become invested with a new interest, for it has been discovered that they bear a great deal of uranium, not richly concentrated but in amounts that make the area a significant reserve for future development.

The uranium lies in beds of lignite, a carbonaceous material sometimes called "brown coal." The curious relationship between uranium and coal has been known since 1875, when E. L. Berthoud noted that carbonaceous material had a high affinity for uranium. Recent laboratory experiments have shown that peat, lignite and subbituminous coal can extract more than 98 per cent of the uranium in a liquid solution of uranium sulfate. Other organic materials such as wood and tricalcium phosphate also can extract substantial percentages of uranium from solution. In the field geologists have observed that nearly all the uranium deposits in the Colorado Plateau, the chief source of that vital mineral in the U. S., contain a great deal of organic material in the form of fossil wood and other plant debris.

When the intensive reconnaissance for uranium began in the U. S. toward the end of World War II, it seemed logical to check coal, lignite and other carbon-rich beds with Geiger counters. In 1948 D. G. Wyant and E. P. Beroni of the U. S. Geological Survey, working on behalf of the Atomic Energy Commission, discovered promising levels of radioactivity in various beds of lignite in northwestern South Dakota, southwestern North Dakota and eastern Montana. They recommended exploration of this material, and analyses of many samples showed that the lignite did indeed contain uranium. These detailed studies are still in progress and provide the basis for this account. The principal contributors have been H. L. Bauer, Jr., N. M. Denson, G. O. Bachman, H. D. Zeller, J. R. Gill, G. W. Moore and J. M. Schopf, all of the Geological Survey. The investigations are being conducted for the Atomic Energy Commission.

The region in which the uranium-bearing lignites were found has had a long and complex geologic history. Upon a basement consisting of very old igneous and metamorphic rocks inland seas and rivers deposited many different sedimentary formations during the long Paleozoic and Mesozoic eras. About sixty million years ago, when the continent had been uplifted sufficiently to put an end to the seas' flooding of large areas in the interior, the northern Great Plains became a region of vast swamps in which plant life flourished, died and accumulated to form peat beds. These swamps were buried from time to time by sands and clays washed in by rivers from the Rocky Mountains region. As the peat beds were buried deeper and deeper, they were slowly transformed into lignite, but the transformation in this region did not go far enough to produce bituminous or anthracite coal.

Eventually these strata, which geologists call the Fort Union formation, were rather abruptly tilted northward by a general uplift and warping of the earth's crust. The surface was then beveled nearly flat again by stream erosion. Now came a new series of deposits, this time consisting of sand with considerable amounts of very fine volcanic ash, probably from volcanoes to the west. These younger deposits were laid across the tilted and eroded edges of the older sediments. Later stream erosion stripped away almost all of the sand-ash mantle. The only remnants of it now left are the buttes, which, with their sheer sides and caps of hard rock, stand like the pebble-capped little mounds of earth you see on bare ground after a hard rain.

This, then, is a capsule history of the way in which the buttes were formed; the history is written in their strata, which include beds of lignite as much as twenty feet thick. Exploring these lignites as potential ores of uranium was quite a new experience and a new kind of economic geology, even for experienced coal geologists. Uranium-bearing coal looks no different from ordinary coal except in rare instances when associated minerals discolor interfaces in the layers. To find out whether a lignite bed contains uranium, and how much, one must scan it with a radiation-measuring instrument, such as the Geiger or the scintillation counter, and then analyze any radioactive samples by extremely sensitive chemical assays. Many radiation measurements and chemical analyses for uranium have been made of samples from Dakota lignites to determine the amount of uranium in various beds and parts of the same bed.

How did the uranium get into the lignite in the first place? One theory is that it was present in solution in the water of the original swamps, having been carried there by streams from distant areas. If there were significant quantities of uranium in the swamp water, it is logical to believe that the uranium would be abstracted from solution by the woody material, just as happens in the laboratory when wood is immersed in a uranium solution. This theory. however, seems to leave several questions unanswered. Denson, Bachman and Zeller ot the Geological Survey have suggested what seems to be a much more likely explanation. They noticed that of the different lignite beds in a butte only the highest one contained a significant percentage of uranium and, furthermore, uranium tended to be more abundant at the top of the bed than farther down. This indicated strongly that the uranium had trickled down from above. Tests with counters showed that the volcanic rocks overlying the lignite were indeed radioactive. (The sand and volcanic ash deposits are called the White River and Arikaree formations.) Apparently ground water dissolved uranium in these beds and washed it down into the highest lignite bed. Every time rain fell, some of it percolated through pores and cracks in the uranium-bearing volcanic ash and carried uranium down in solution to the lignite. Because of the affinity of uranium for carbonaceous material, the lignite extracted the uranium from the solution. One confirmation of this theory is the fact that water in springs around the margins of the buttes is radioactive, showing clearly that uranium is still being dissolved from the volcanic rocks. It now becomes apparent why uranium-bearing lignites have been found only near and beneath the buttes of the region. In the intervening broad lowlands, erosion has removed all the volcanic cap rock and also the highest lignite beds, which would have captured most of the uranium. Only in the vicinity of the buttes are these highest lignite beds still preserved.

This hypothesis of the origin of the uranium-bearing lignites in the Dakota region has prompted geologists of the Geological Survey to explore for uranium-bearing coals and carbonaceous shales in other regions where beds of this type are known to be in proximity to beds containing volcanic ash. A number of other deposits have been found in areas where this favorable set of geologic conditions exists. The theory gives geologists a guide for exploration which is an improvement over mere random sampling of carbonaceous deposits.

The process described is certainly not the only mechanism by which uranium deposits have been formed, even in carbonaceous beds. Each new deposit found has to be interpreted in the light of the geologic history of the region in which it lies, and each one presents its own peculiarities and its own problems of origin.

In comparison with other sources of uranium that are being mined or developed today, the Dakota lignites are very low grade. No efficient or inexpensive means of extracting the uranium from them has yet been found. Nevertheless, the tonnages of uranium in the lignites are large and thus form a reserve of considerable strategic value, particularly if the U. S. were to be cut off from foreign sources of supply in a time of national emergency. For these reasons it has seemed important to the Atomic Energy Commission and to the Geological Survey to learn as much as possible about the potential of uranium from coal. Thousands of outcrops of coal beds have been examined by Survey geologists, and many of them have been sampled. In addition, diamond-drill holes have been put down at strategic locations by the Geological Survey and the Bureau of Mines to probe the ore possibilities in beds below the surface.

Mining of these deposits for uranium is not likely in the near future, in view of their low grade. It seems, however, that increasing demands for uranium, coupled with development of new inexpensive metallurgical techniques for recovering the uranium, will eventually result in their exploitation. That day may be accelerated if industries decide to utilize the lignites in large quantities for fuel and recover the uranium from the otherwise worthless ash as a by-product.

PART 3 FUEL AND FISSION PRODUCTS

I. REACTOR CHEMISTRY

by John F. Flagg and Edwin L. Zebroski

The authors were collaborating at the Knolls Laboratories of the General Electric Company on the engineering and research problems they are concerned with here when they wrote this chapter in 1952. John F. Flagg was born in Wellsville, New York, in 1914, was educated at the University of Rochester and at Princeton University, where he got his doctorate in analytical chemistry. He is now manager of the chemical and chemical engineering divisions of the atomic power laboratory at Knolls. Edwin L. Zebroski was born in Chicago in 1921, got his bachelor's degree at the University of Chicago and his doctorate at the University of California. He is now manager of nuclear engineering at Stanford Research Institute.

II. FISSION PRODUCTS

by Paul J. Lovewell

A professional in administration, Paul J. Lovewell is director of economics research at Stanford Research Institute. A native of Topeka, Kansas, he graduated from Washburn University in 1938 and went on to take his master's degree in the Graduate School of Business at Stanford University. He has had a varied experience in business and industry and, during the war, in the supplies and accounts bureau of the U. S. Navy. Since he first joined the staff of the Stanford Research Institute in 1948, Lovewell has conducted more than thirty "techno-economic" studies of the kind that supports this chapter on the possibilities of fission products.

REACTOR CHEMISTRY

by John F. Flagg and Edwin L. Zebroski

How soon atomic power will become available at reasonable cost depends on many things, but one of the most decisive is a matter of chemistry. The whole issue may turn on whether we can succeed in obtaining reasonably complete "combustion" of the nuclear fuel.

The "burning" of uranium in an atomic furnace is so strange an affair that to get any picture of it at all we must overturn our familiar ideas about the behavior of a fuel. Let us try to see how it contrasts with a conventional fuel such as coal. Imagine a lump of coal in which only a tiny proportion of the lump (one part in 140) is combustible. The combustible atoms are scattered all through the lump. As each burns, it gives off sparks that ignite others, and the burning proceeds by a chain reaction. But the ashes of the burned atoms, deposited throughout the lump, soon begin to absorb some of the sparks and smother the fire. Furthermore, as the proportion of combustible material drops, the chances of the sparks hitting enough inflammable atoms to keep the fire going also drop.

The result is that the fire goes out and the lump of coal becomes useless as fuel after only a small percentage of its combustible material has been used up. Yet we are dealing with an expensive kind of coal, and we cannot afford to throw away most of it unburned. We must take the lump of coal out of the furnace, remove the ashes from it and recover the unused fuel. Moreover, there is another reason for reprocessing the coal. During the burning, some of the noncombustible material in the lump has absorbed sparks from the fire and thereby has been converted to usable fuel. This precious material also must be recovered; indeed, unless the furnace manufactures, or "breeds," more new fuel than was originally put in, our rare coal may be too expensive altogether.

The business of reprocessing the coal is not an ordinary chemical operation. The lumps of coal are so "hot" that they have to be placed behind several feet of concrete and treated by remote control. The lumps must be dissolved and put through a series of complicated chemical separations. The ashes are present in such tiny amounts that we must mix in a chemically similar "carrier" material to give them enough bulk so they can be precipitated from a solution. The new fuel bred in the furnace also is minute in amount and difficult to separate. As for the coal itself, we cannot separate the combustible from the noncombustible material by any chemical process, because they are chemically identical.

After removing the ashes and recovering and purifying the fuel, we put it back in the furnace to burn some more. It begins burning briskly but soon dies down, so that we must take it out and refine it again. Thus to burn all or most of the fuel in our lump of coal we must reprocess and feed it into the furnace again and again and again, each time adding fresh fuel to keep the fire going.

The strange coal we have been describing is, of course, uranium; the combustion process is nuclear fission. Uranium 235 is the primary nuclear fuel, the only fissionable material found in nature. Refined natural uranium consists of a mixture of 140 parts of non-fissionable U-238 to one part of fissionable U-235. A U-235 atom fissions when it captures a slow neutron—the spark of our analogy. In breaking apart it liberates energy, emits two or three new neutrons (average: 2.5), and leaves as "ash" its fragmentary remains, or fission products. One neutron must be captured by another atom of U-235 to keep the chain reaction going; the other one or two neutrons are available for other reactions. If they are captured by U-238, they convert these atoms into fissionable plutonium, which may itself be used for fuel. In a breeder reactor, plutonium would be manufactured in a blanket of natural uranium wrapped around the "firebox" (reactor core) to capture the excess neutrons.

A uranium furnace is rather more complicated than our coal analogy indicated. The fuel itself is damaged by the radiations in the pile—another reason why it must be reprocessed. In some reactors the uranium lumps are encased in aluminum, which must be removed from the fuel in reprocessing. The furnace also contains a moderator (graphite or heavy water), a cooling liquid to transfer the heat to the steam boiler where it is to be used, and an array of controls and safety devices. All these materials are subjected to neutron bombardment, which gradually changes their physical properties.

The Hanford Plutonium Works, the only production-scale reactor installation in the U. S., originally had no provision for recovering unburned uranium; after plutonium was extracted from the uranium slugs, the remaining material was discharged to waste tanks—fission products, unused U-235 and all. Where power is the objective, any economic plant will have to have a complete processing plant, which will be as essential as the reactor itself. Research on fuel processing has been going forward, concurrently with the development of power reactors. Some of the processing problems can be discussed outside the realm of security restrictions.

Let us assume that a reactor has reached the point where it must be shut down and its fuel discharged. The fuel slugs contain a mixture of U-238, U-235, plutonium and fission products. To appreciate the problems involved in separating these materials, let us see what quantities we have to deal with. Plutonium and fission products are manufactured in roughly equal amounts, at a rate which depends on the power level at which the reactor operates. For every 1,000 kilowatt-day of energy production, approximately one gram of U-235 is fissioned. This means there will be one gram of fission products and about one gram of plutonium, thinly distributed in a considerable bulk of uranium slugs. In one and one-half tons of uranium, after 100,000 kilowatt-days of operation, there would be only about ¼ pound of plutonium and ¼ pound of fission products. And in this relatively tiny amount of fission products there may be more than 200 isotopes of 34 different elements, ranging from zinc to europium in the periodic table.

When the reactor is shut down, the fuel slugs are pushed out of the pile into a deep pool of water—a shield to contain their intense radioactivity. The slugs must be left in the pool for several months to cool off: that is, to allow some of the hottest isotopes, of short half-life, to decay. Then the slugs, behind thick concrete shields, are dissolved, and the separation process can begin.

Several separation methods are available. One is precipitation. To precipitate the tiny traces of plutonium and fission-product elements in the solution, one must introduce carrier substances chemically similar to them. Lanthanum acts as a carrier for plutonium. In the solution both the uranium and plutonium ions are in the oxidized state, with a valence of plus six. A reducing agent such as sulfur dioxide is added to reduce the plutonium to a valence of plus three or four. Now lanthanum nitrate is added and then hydrogen fluoride. This precipitates lanthanum fluoride, and with it the reduced plutonium and some of the fission products—the rare earths. The other fission products and uranium remain in the solution and are filtered off. The precipitate is then redissolved and an oxidizing agent added, which brings the plutonium back to the plus six state. Lanthanum fluoride is again precipitated, but this time only the fission products come down; the oxidized plutonium remains in solution.

Precipitation processes offer the advantage of flexibility and easy expansion of the laboratory procedures to production-scale operation. The yields, however, may not be as high as with other separation procedures. Precipitation is an expensive way to recover uranium, because of the engineering difficulties in handling precipitates in large tonnages.

A second possible separation method is ion exchange. Washed through large beds of synthetic resin exchanger, the mixed solution of fuel could be separated into its uranium, plutonium and fission products. Ion exchange has already been used successfully to separate rare earths and trans-plutonium elements having very similar chemical properties. It has the advantage of being relatively simple, both as to operations and equipment. But in a production-scale operation large volumes of liquids would have to be handled, and the radioactive fission products might damage the exchange resins.

The third method is solvent extraction. It makes use of differences in the solubility of substances in different solvents. Long used in the petroleum industry, the technique was first applied in the nuclear field to purify large tonnages of uranium for the reactors. Uranium nitrate, when mixed with a "salting agent" such as calcium nitrate, is much more soluble in ether than in water; alone, it is more soluble in water. If a water solution of the uranium salt uranyl nitrate, in the presence of calcium nitrate, is pumped through a packed column in one direction while ether is sent through from the other end, the ether will take up most of the uranium salt, leaving impurities in the water. The uranium can then be "stripped" from the ether with water in the absence of the calcium salting agent. By repeated extraction and water-strips uranium can be be refined to a high degree of purity.

In the same way the uranium and plutonium in reactor slugs could be separated from fission products. Plutonium might then be separated from uranium by reducing the former to the plus three state, in which it is insoluble in ether.

Solvent extraction gives sharp separations and can be carried out either by continuous or batch operation. But the method involves special problems of protection. In addition to the usual hazard of fire or explosion of the volatile solvent, there is the possibility of a resulting spread of radioactivity. Another disadvantage is that very large volumes of solution would have to be handled and stored.

In practice it may be best to use a combination of separation methods, for example, solvent extraction and ion exchange or carrier precipitation.

The disposal of radioactive wastes will be one of the big factors in the operation of atomic power plants. One suggestion is that the radioisotopes might be converted into a stable "mineral" and buried out of the way by incorporating them into a special concrete or ceramic.

We have been considering only uranium as the nuclear fuel. Thorium also is a fertile material; when irradiated with neutrons, it is transmuted into fissionable uranium 233. The problems of recovering thorium and U-233 do not differ greatly from those of uranium.

What of the design of the processing plant? The chemical separation methods must be highly efficient, for every ounce of the fuel is precious. A single pound of U-235 can produce $15,000 worth of electricity, assuming a heat yield of about 10 million kilowatt-hours, 30 per cent efficiency in converting the heat into electricity, and a price of 5 mills per kilowatt-hour. Since the fuel may have to be reprocessed 10 times or more, a small loss at any stage of the cycle would be multiplied.

The processing plant will require huge buildings and intricate networks of equipment and instruments. Many operations will have to be performed behind concrete shields by remote control. Ordinary commercial equipment, which needs continual maintenance to keep it functioning properly, will not do for these operations. The components will have to be specially designed for maximum reliability. When a breakdown does occur, the faulty piece will have to be removed and replaced *in toto* rather than repaired. Aside from the radioactivity problem, plutonium is extremely poisonous, and great care must be taken to avoid breathing it in the form of dust or fumes.

Furthermore, it must be borne in mind that we are dealing with a fuel which flares up spontaneously whenever it reaches a critical mass. About two pounds of U-235 in water will sustain a chain reaction. Though it would not blow up in a bomb-type explosion, the heat and radiation could be disastrous. Hence we must be sure that nowhere in the maze of tanks, pipes and other equipment could a critical mass of fissionable material ever accumulate, by any possible combination of equipment failure and human error. This means that there is a limit to the possible size of the equipment, and hence to the economies realizable from large-scale operation.

Processing will certainly represent a substantial part of the cost of atomic power. Elsewhere in this book, two authorities give widely disparate estimates of the cost of uranium fuel: Lawrence Hafstad places the cost at more than one mill per kilowatt-hour, and Sam H. Schurr calculates it would cost less than .02 mills per kilowatt-hour of electrical energy generated. Hafstad's figure is based on separated U-235, while Schurr assumes 100 per cent conversion of U-238 to plutonium and charges reprocessing to operating costs rather than to the cost of fuel. The 50-fold difference between their figures may be taken as a rough index to the economic role of processing.

In short, the realization of atomic power will depend heavily on the chemist and the chemical engineer. The opportunities are great, the stakes high.

FISSION PRODUCTS

by Paul J. Lovewell

A GRAM of radium, with one curie of radioactivity, is worth $15,000 to $20,000. In the waste tanks of the Hanford plutonium works lie millions of gallons of radioactive material, representing millions of curies, and day by day this vast store of potentially valuable radiant energy continues to pile up uselessly. Indeed, up to now it has been worse than useless: its disposal has been a headache.

The problem of how to turn this dangerous liability into a national asset has occupied the time and thought of a great many atomic energy workers during the past few years. From the outset one of the chief aims has been to find ways to put it to work in industry. The chief questions are: What could it do, and how could it be harnessed safely? To these questions we now have some carefully studied answers. This article will report some of the findings of the most comprehensive analysis made to date—a survey carried out by the Stanford Research Institute for the Atomic Energy Commission with the aid and consultation of scores of scientists and engineers in universities and in industry.

Before discussing the industrial possibilities, we need to consider the nature of this strange, potent material that it is proposed to introduce into U. S. industry. It consists of the fission products formed as by-products of the operation of an atomic pile. When uranium 235 atoms split, they break down into a number of different medium-weight elements—iodine, barium, strontium, zirconium, cesium, cerium and so on. These radioactive fission products must be removed from the pile from time to time, because they act as ashes smothering the chain reaction. After being separated chemically from uranium and plutonium, the fission products are left mixed together in solution. For some industrial purposes this mixture, partly refined, could be used, but for many applications it will probably be necessary to extract individual elements.

The radioactive fission products emit gamma and beta rays. The uses to which such radiations may be put are varied: they can kill bacteria, make "X-ray" pictures of metals, measure thicknesses, trigger chemical reactions, speed the travel of a flame, ionize air, and perform a host of other functions. An X-ray machine or radium or radioisotopes made by irradiating materials inserted into a pile can do the same things, but the great importance of the fission products is that they make radioactivity available on a vastly larger scale and at much lower cost.

Just how much fission products would cost is hard to determine, because we do not yet know on what terms the atomic energy enterprise would provide them or how expensive it would be to process them. But some of the best engineering opinion places the probable cost in the range of a few cents to a few dollars per curie. At such prices the use of radioactivity would become feasible for a very wide range of industrial purposes. Some of the more attractive possibilities are:

Sterilization. Radioactivity might have a very large field in processing foods and drugs. Heat, the treatment now generally used to kill bacteria and preserve food, destroys some of the nutrients and changes the flavor. With radioactivity, food processors could sterilize food without heat. The food would be exposed after packaging to radioactive material (a mixture of fission products would do) in an enclosed, shielded space. There would be no danger of the food becoming radioactive, because the gamma and beta emissions from fission products do not induce radioactivity. The penetrating gamma radiation would kill all organisms in the food, and no bacteria could get into the sealed package. Thus some foods that now need to be refrigerated after packaging could be kept at room temperature. Radioactivity could also be used to sterilize the surface of fresh foods that are not treated at all now, such as tomatoes, apples, oranges, melons, grapes and eggs. A relatively rapid treatment of the surface, where the organisms could be killed even by the non-penetrating beta rays, would prolong the shelf life of these foods and reduce the need for refrigeration.

In the case of certain drugs, the use of heat for sterilization is out of the question, for heat destroys their properties. Consequently such medicinals as the antibiotics, blood fractions, surgical dressings and vaccines now have to be prepared and handled by very costly aseptic techniques. Cold sterilization with fission products would make all these products much easier to handle and insure 100 per cent sterility.

The radioactive sterilization of foods would have commercial possibilities if fission products were available at a few cents per curie, and for drugs it would be feasible at up to $2 per curie.

Radiography. The inspection of metals for internal flaws is another important job for penetrating radiation. Its value to industry is already so well recognized that X-rays, radium or radio-cobalt are commonly used to inspect castings and assembled machinery. Fission products, notably such gamma-emitters as cesium 137, could do the same job at lower cost. Even at a price of $5 to $50 per curie, radiography could feasibly be extended to inspection of a wide range of industrial materials, opening a demand for hundreds of thousands of curies. This could mean better, safer, lighter, stronger or cheaper metals and metal articles.

Luminescence. Phosphorescent paints that glow in the dark all depend upon radiant energy. They are now expensive, because they are made with radium or radioisotopes. A fission product such as strontium 90, even at $50 per curie, would bring down the cost substantially. If luminiscent markers were really cheap, a wide market might open up: e.g., for exit signs in theaters, advertising displays, highway markers, cellar stairways, and so forth.

Static Elimination. Static electricity is a hazard or a nuisance in many industrial processes. In printing, for example, charges build up on sheets of paper, causing them to stick together or repel each other. One way to prevent the build-up of static charges on objects is to ionize the air around them; ionized air, being a good conductor, takes off the electricity as fast as it forms. Static eliminators containing radium or polonium are now on the market, but here again fission products, such as strontium 90, offer a cheaper substitute.

Measurement. By passing radiation through a layer of material whose absorbing qualities are known, and measuring the amount of absorption, the thickness of the layer can be determined. Thickness gauges which operate on this principle have already been built. Fission products in laboratory amounts are finding a market in instruments of this kind even at prices of $100 per curie.

Chemistry. In the chemical industry radioactivity may make possible completely new products. Beta and gamma radiations break up molecules into reactive fractions which can form new molecules that could not otherwise be synthesized.

Combustion. Since flames are propagated by the interaction of ions, fission products, by virtue of their ionizing ability, can speed up or control burning processes. This could lead to significant improvements in jet and internal combustion engines.

Power. A radioactive material can generate small amounts of electrical power. If a pure beta emitter is placed on an insulating post in an evacuated tube, it will build up to a high positive voltage as it loses beta particles (electrons), and the voltage may be tapped for power. Although the power that can practicably be obtained in this way is small (up to one watt), such a unit can go on generating for years without refueling or maintenance. One possible use for a generator of this kind is to power instruments, such as weather recorders, that could be left in remote locations.

Various other more speculative possibilities for the use of radioactivity have been considered. It might be employed to control and stimulate the fermentation process in converting grain starches to alcohol, to prevent fermentation in drilling muds, to control weevils and other insect pests in stored seeds and grain, to stop insect contamination of packaged flour, to protect underground cables against fungi that destroy the insulation and to guard instruments against fungus growth, a serious problem in the tropics.

This brief summary by no means exhausts all the possibilities for the use of fission products. One thing it indicates is that in the immediate future the fission products are most likely to be helpful to existing industries, making possible better and cheaper production of their goods, rather than to bring into being new products or new industries. Any large-scale introduction of these new tools into industry would, however, create a few new business opportunities from the start: the processing of fission products, the manufacture of protective shielding, radiation engineering services for manufacturers.

Shielding, of course, will be one of the major problems. Cold sterilization would have to be carried out behind several feet of concrete. Any radioactive material exposed in public places, as in luminous signs, would need to be sealed to hold in its radiation. The signs would probably take the form of a plastic sandwich, with the fission products and glowing phosphors buried in the middle. The shielding expense was taken into account in estimating the costs of the various uses of fission products.

Costs will play the major part, of course, in determining how widely these new tools are accepted by industry. In general, fission-product radiation will be more expensive than heat in any application for which either may be used; for example, food sterilized by radiation may cost more than food sterilized by heat or preserved by cold. On the other hand, radiation may have compensating advantages. Fission products will also be in competition with other sources of radiation, such as X-ray machines and Van de Graaff generators. It appears that fission-product radiation would be a good deal cheaper than X-radiation; at $2 per curie the former would deliver energy at about two cents per watt-hour as against 20 cents to $1 per watt-hour for the tube alone in the case of X-rays. But radiation-producing machines have certain important advantages: they can be turned on and off; they can vary the energy and quantity of their radiation output; they present no waste-disposal problem, as do depleted fission products. For some applications, such as the surface sterilization of foods, Van de Graaff generators, which fire a beam of high-energy electrons, may be more economical than fission products.

A multitude of important technical and economic problems remain to be solved before fission products can be profitably used by industry on any large scale. One of the first major steps must be to select the best process for refining fission products. This will be a multi-million-dollar decision, because it will mean the construction of special facilities. But until it is done, industry will be frustrated in efforts to evaluate the fission products' usefulness. For some of the necessary tests they need much larger amounts of radioactive material than are now obtainable. A cold-sterilization pilot plant, for example, would require perhaps 100,000 to one million curies.

Studies of many of the problems connected with the use of fission products are, however, under way. The Brookhaven National Laboratory now has thousand-curie sources of cobalt 60 and tantalum 182 which are available to industry for irradiation of prepackaged materials. Many companies have already indicated interest in this service, and a number of actual tests have been run.

A similar service will be set up in other parts of the country. Development-scale facilities for production of strontium 90 and cesium 137 are being built at the Oak Ridge National Laboratory. A supply of cesium 137 providing 1,500 to 2,000 curies is to be produced and given to the Oak Ridge Institute for Nuclear Studies for industrial research. Data from the operation of these facilities may be used in designing a fission-product plant for mass production of 1,000-curie sources of strontium 90 and cerium 144.

The General Electric Company and Oak Ridge are both working on the problem of preparing and packaging large quantities of radioactivity. The Massachusetts Institute of Technology, Columbia University and the University of Michigan are studying the irradiation of foods, to determine, among other things, its possible effects on taste and toxicity. At the Stanford Research Institute there will soon be under way a research program to develop the process engineering for sterilization of both drugs and foods, to work out industrial radiography systems, to investigate chemical reactions activated by gamma rays and to offer a radiation service to industry. Yale University and Columbia are working on radiation chemistry. Michigan is studying the ionizing effects of radiation on flame propagation.

Even if only some of the uses for radioactive wastes suggested in this chapter prove feasible, the problem may become not what to do with the fission products but how to obtain a big enough supply of them. At all events, the great stocks of radioactive material now lying idle in our storage tanks constitute a national resource that challenges our industrial ingenuity and can open new technological frontiers.

PART 4 ECONOMICS AND POLITICS

I. THE PRICE PER KILOWATT-HOUR

by Sam H. Schurr

This chapter is the fruit of the first major investigation of the economics of atomic power conducted under the auspices of the Cowles Commission at the University of Chicago by Jacob Marschak and the author. Sam H. Schurr is now director of the Energy and Mineral Resources Program of Resources for the Future, Inc., a recently organized conservation group. He was educated at Rutgers and Columbia universities and, at different times, has been a member of the economics staff of the National Bureau of Economic Research, the RAND Corporation, the Office of Strategic Services, and the Bureau of Labor Statistics, his last government appointment being that of Chief Economist of the U. S. Bureau of Mines. Schurr's special field of study is the relationship between general economic development and progress in technology.

II. THE ATOMIC ENERGY ACT OF 1954

by David F. Cavers

At Harvard Law School, David F. Cavers holds a dual appointment as Fessenden Professor of Law and Associate Dean. After graduating from the University of Pennsylvania and getting his law degree at Harvard in 1926, he practiced law for three years in New York City, then taught law successively at Harvard, West Virginia and Duke. At Duke, he established and was for ten years editor of the quarterly *Law and Contemporary Problems*. At Harvard, Dean Cavers is primarily concerned with the Law School's research activities and its program of international legal studies.

III. INTERNATIONAL CO-OPERATION

by Donald J. Hughes

Ever since the first atomic pile went into operation at the University of Chicago in 1943, Donald J. Hughes has been working with nuclear reactors. Born in Chicago in 1915, he was educated at the University of Chicago, receiving his Ph.D. in 1940. He had a brief interim as a developer of mine and torpedo detectors before he joined the Manhattan District and settled in the field of nuclear physics to stay. With a background that includes work on the Hanford piles and a term as director of the nuclear physics division of the Argonne National Laboratory, he is now senior physicist in charge of a group doing reactor and neutron research at Brookhaven National Laboratory.

THE PRICE PER KILOWATT-HOUR

by Sam H. Schurr

In the present state of international tension any analysis of the peaceful possibilities of atomic power admittedly must take a long view. No one can close his eyes to the fact that the political and military aspects of atomic energy will dominate all other aspects for some time to come.

The Cowles Commission study of the economics of atomic power, which this chapter summarizes, in the main excluded political questions and assumed a state of affairs in which the development of atomic power could proceed without artificial hindrances. The complexity of the subject demands this approach. Science often finds it must separate the variables in a problem and consider them independently if it is to handle the problem at all. This is certainly the situation in the complex field of atomic energy.

Attempts to depict the future of the "atomic age" have tended to run to two poles. At one extreme, enthusiasts have pictured a world in which nuclear energy will drive our cars and round-the-world airplanes, blast aside mountains and break up icecaps, heat our homes and kill our germs, power our railroads and run our factories, control our weather and transport us to the moon. At the other, pessimists have asserted that atomic power will never be practical except for a very limited kind of use. Our study attempted to make a realistic appraisal of the economic feasibility of the use of atomic power on the basis of the present estimated range of costs and present concepts of nuclear technology. We therefore left out of account problematic future developments (e.g., the possibility that nuclear energy might be converted directly into electricity) and restricted our analysis to a single type of plant—a heat-and-electricity generating station in which the conventional furnace would be replaced by a nuclear-fission reactor.

Now in such a plant we are dealing with something that is partly new but not altogether so. It differs in some fundamental respects from a conventional power plant, but it also has many points of similarity, and the latter give us some known yardsticks for cost comparisons.

One important difference, of course, is in the energy content per pound of fuel. In a conventional plant a pound of coal can be transformed into about one kilowatt-hour of electric power. In a fission-powered plant a pound of atomic fuel would yield about 2.5 million kilowatt-hours of electric power. Assuming that natural uranium (or thorium) could be completely converted into nuclear fuel, of which there seems to be a good chance, this means that a pound of uranium would be the equivalent of approximately 2.5 million pounds, or 1,250 tons, of bituminous coal. Hence in comparison with coal, uranium would be a practically weightless fuel. The cost per unit of energy of transporting atomic fuel would be negligible. The economic importance of this fact is clear: the use of nuclear fuel would tend to equalize the cost of fuel throughout the world.

It follows also that in terms of energy content nuclear fuel is likely to be cheaper than coal. In 1943 relatively pure uranium obtained from good-grade ores cost about $20 per pound. An equivalent amount of coal at $6 per ton, the average price paid by utilities in 1949, would cost $7,500. Nuclear fuel would be considerably cheaper even if low-grade uranium ores were used. For example, even if the cost of pure uranium increased a hundred fold, to $2,000 per pound, it would still be only about one fourth as costly as coal per kilowatt-hour of energy yield.

The two hypotheses just stated—that nuclear fuel might be available everywhere in the world at about the same cost and that this might be a very low cost—determined the fundamental orientation of the Cowles Commission study. Our analysis was concerned mainly with the possible economic effects of ubiquitous, low-cost power.

But fuel is only one element in the cost and availability of power. The construction and operating costs of the plant in which the fuel is burned must also be taken into account. Since it is not yet possible to calculate those costs with any definiteness, we considered a range of cost possibilities, as estimated by various authorities who have considered the problem. We made the costs from these different sources as comparable with each other and with the cost of power from conventional sources, in terms of certain common cost elements, as the data permitted. We chose the price levels of 1946 as the basis for the comparison. Although the general price level has risen considerably since then, the relation between the prices of the materials needed in atomic and conventional power plants has not changed substantially, so the comparison is still valid.

The hypothetical atomic power plant chosen for analysis is a central electricity-generating station with a capacity of 75,000 kilowatts operating at 50 per cent of capacity—a reasonable average level of operation for such a plant. On this basis three estimates of the possible cost of producing atomic electricity were arrived at: low, intermediate and high. The minimum, below which the cost cannot possibly fall, is 4 to 4.5 mills per kilowatt-hour. The intermediate figure is 6.5 to 7 mills per kilowatt-hour. The highest estimated figure for the cost of atomic power is about 10 mills per kilowatt-hour.

It must be emphasized that these figures are only rough estimates. We can be reasonably sure, however, that the minimum will not fall below 4 mills. We know that the atomic power plant will require certain equipment, such as turbines and the like, that a conventional generating plant uses, and these would represent a considerable proportion of the total cost of the plant. The 4-mills minimum is based on the assumption that the capital investment per kilowatt in a nuclear-powered plant would be no higher than that in a coal-fueled plant.

The firm minimum estimate is a very useful figure because it tells us the utmost that may be expected of atomic power. It thereby enables us to determine where it would *not* be economical to use it even under the most favorable circumstances and also indicates the nature of changes that might take place.

We have evaluated these estimates in terms of an approximate time scale. The highest figure we take to represent the cost in the first commercial plants producing atomic power. The intermediate cost figures we consider to represent an approximation of the level of costs which might prevail in plants built, say, five to ten years after the first commercial installations. These plants would incorporate the improvements based on the lessons learned in constructing and operating the earliest plants, but would still fall short of the most efficient designs that might ultimately be achieved after many years of experience. The lowest figure represents the minimum cost at which atomic electricity could ever be produced by techniques considered likely at the present time.

Now how do these figures compare with the cost of generating electricity in conventional coal-burning plants? For this comparison we used prewar prices of coal, which of course were considerably lower than they are today, because they were the only satisfactory figures available on a worldwide basis. We estimated what generating costs would be in a large coal-burning plant (75,000 to 100,000 kilowatts) of the most modern design operating at 50 per cent of capacity. Assuming that the plant was located close to an exceptionally low-cost mine that produced coal at the low price of $1.50 per ton, it could generate power at 4.5 mills per kilowatt-hour. In the prewar decade coal was mined at this price in some sections of the U. S., Great Britain, the U.S.S.R., Manchuria, China, India and South Africa. But this was unusual. The average cost of coal at the mine in the U. S. as a whole was about $2 per ton. At that price the cost of generating electricity in a modern plant near the mine would be between 4.5 and 5 mills per kilowatt-hour. The typical cost in plants at the mine mouth around the world would be about 5 to 5.5 mills.

Of course the cost rises as the distance of the plant from the mine increases. In the U. S. in 1937 the average freight charge for delivering coal to plants was $2.17 per net ton—more than the mining cost itself. A representative railroad freight charge for a haul of 500 miles was $4.13 per ton. Reckoning in this transportation cost, a power plant 500 miles from the mine would produce electricity at 6.5 mills per kilowatt-hour.

Shipping coal by water is, of course, much less expensive per ton-mile than by railroad, but the cost generally is still considerable because of the long distances involved. For instance, the coal shipping charges in 1937 from Great Britain to various ports in Brazil and Argentina ranged from $3.20 to $3.60 per ton. The price of British coal at these ports ranged from $7.80 to $8.20 per ton, and at many cities far from the coast it was $10.50 or more. At these prices it would cost about 7 mills per kilowatt-hour to produce electricity in a model plant in a port city of Brazil or Argentina and more than 8 mills in an inland city of those countries.

It is clear, then, that in comparison with electricity produced in coal-burning plants at the mine mouth (at 1937 coal prices) atomic power would be competitive only if available at a cost near the minimum estimate. But at a distance of 500 rail miles from the mine in the U. S., atomic energy could compete with coal if it could produce electricity at the estimated intermediate cost. And in Brazil and Argentina electricity costs based on British coal approach the highest cost estimates of atomic power. In other words, the economic feasibility of atomic power, and its effects, will depend primarily on geography.

A major part of our research was devoted to analyzing the possible effects of low-cost atomic power on individual industries. These industries were aluminum, chlorine and caustic soda, phosphate fertilizer, cement, brick, flat glass, iron and steel, railroad transportation and residential heating. All of them are, or could become, important consumers of energy.

In analyzing each industry we asked three major questions: 1) Would atomic power bring about an important reduction in its production costs? 2) Would it encourage the introduction of new production techniques? 3) Would it change the industry's present geographical pattern?

Our findings on these questions vary considerably from industry to industry, but certain significant generalizations are possible. The most significant is that in the U. S. atomic power probably will not have important effects on the industries studied unless it can be made available at a cost near the estimated minimum. Even at this low cost for power, production costs in the industries concerned would not be greatly reduced. But in several cases, assuming that atomic power does become available at the minimum estimated costs, savings might be enough to encourage changes in production processes or relocation of factories.

The possible effects can best be illustrated by considering a particular industry. Let us take iron and steel. Iron ore smelting today is completely dependent on coal in the form of coke. In smelting coal acts both as a source of heat and as a chemical agent. Energy is also required in the later stages of steel manufacture, such as steel refining and rolling. Obviously it is highly advantageous, to obtain the greatest fuel economy, to carry on all these operations at the same place. Consequently the pattern has been to combine coke ovens, blast furnaces, steel furnaces and rolling mills in one group of works at a single site. Coal has thus had a powerful influence in dictating the geographical concentration of the iron and steel industry in the U. S.

Atomic power might alter the pattern in one or both of the following ways: 1) it might replace coke as a blast furnace fuel, thereby releasing the entire operation from its fundamental dependence on coal, since the other processes could operate on other fuels; 2) it might simply separate the steel furnace and rolling mill from the blast furnace, with important effects on those later operations.

We have noted that in the blast furnace coke serves as a chemical reducing agent as well as fuel. But there is on the horizon another reducing technique which might be economically feasible in the U. S. This method would use hydrogen as the reducing agent rather than carbon; it would reduce iron ore to sponge iron. The process, just emerging from the laboratory, is considered promising by the research metallurgists who have experimented with it.

Atomic electricity could be used to produce hydrogen by the electrolysis of water. How would the two reduction methods compare in cost? Obviously only an extremely rough comparison can be made, since the hydrogen method has not yet been tried commercially. Our calculations indicate that the hydrogen method could not compete with the coke blast furnace in present steel centers, which are built close to coal. But if we consider new plants free to locate anywhere, the hydrogen process becomes a possibility. Since no transportation costs to speak of are involved in the use of atomic fuel, the plants could be placed near iron ore. We find that if atomic power could be made available near the estimated minimum cost, reducing plants located in the iron ore region of northern Minnesota might be able to deliver iron to the Chicago-Gary market at a lower cost than the steel plants in that area, and could almost match the cost of iron in the Pittsburgh region.

This particular result rests on assumptions which may prove invalid, particularly with respect to the relative costs of transporting iron ore and sponge iron. It at least raises the possibility, however, that in new plants to be built in the future the hydrogen reduction process might be brought within economic reach.

If the hydrogen process based on atomic electricity should be adopted, it might have major effects on the location and size of steel-producing facilities. The use of by-product gases from the coal would no longer be of great importance, for the hydrogen reduction process would not yield anything like the volume of hot gases exhausted by the coke oven and blast furnace. This change would weaken one of the most important factors which has historically made for the integration of all operations from the coke oven through the rolling mill. On the basis of the hydrogen process, the iron might be reduced at the ore site and the later stages of steel production might be placed near the market for steel products. Furthermore, it appears possible that the hydrogen method could exploit ore resources of about one-tenth the size needed for economic investment in a blast furnace. In time, therefore, the iron-reduction industry might be decentralized, with hydrogen sponge-iron plants developing in various regions, based on local reserves of iron ore.

The other way in which atomic power might affect the steel industry would be the wider employment of processes which enable individual steel plants to operate without depending on the blast furnace or iron ore. For example, atomic power might encourage the electric smelting of steel scrap at new centers. With electrically smelted scrap instead of iron ore as the raw material, a steel plant would not need to be near either iron ore or coal; it could be located wherever abundant scrap supplies existed. Moreover, this development would be assisted by the new process of continuous casting, recently developed experimentally by the Republic Steel Corporation, whereby molten steel is converted to finished shapes in one step, eliminating the making of ingots and billets.

All this might make it possible to build large-scale steel plants in steel-consuming centers, such as New York, Boston and St. Louis, where they are not practical at the present time. The transportation savings derived from producing the steel in the place where it is to be used might well make the utilization of atomic power for scrap smelting worth while. Steel production by this method would of course be limited by the amount of scrap available, which in the near future is not likely to exceed 30 to 40 million tons a year.

So much for iron and steel. The analysis of the other industries showed that changes in production processes or geographical location or both might also occur there, always assuming that atomic power could be made available at a cost near the estimated minimum. Atomic power might, for example, free aluminum production from its ties to cheap hydroelectric power and permit the establishment of aluminum plants in bauxite regions such as Dutch Guiana or in important markets like New York. It might stimulate process changes in the manufacture of phosphate fertilizer, cement and so on.

As for residential heating, although there are a great many *ifs*, it appears that atomic furnaces warrant serious consideration. Space heating is the largest consumer of energy in the U. S.; in 1945 it took almost 20 per cent of our total national energy supply. We considered the economic feasibility of heating houses from district stations where the heat would be produced by nuclear reactors and piped directly (without conversion into electricity) to homes. Experiments in the direct use of heat from a reactor for space heating are already being carried on at the Harwell reactor station in England.

The most important variables affecting the cost of residential district heating are population density and climate. In general, a combination of high population density and cold winters would be required to bring district heating into competition with conventional methods. Our analysis shows that these conditions exist in New York, Chicago, Boston, Buffalo, Milwaukee, Newark and a few other cities, all of which have cold winters and an average population density of more than 13,000 persons per square mile. Not all areas of these cities meet the necessary requirements for economical district heating, but large parts of them undoubtedly do.

The conclusion from our analysis is that atomic furnaces might well compete with conventional heating in these areas. It would not reduce the cost much, if at all, but its convenience (lack of smoke, emancipation of individual householders from their furnaces, and so on) might turn the scale. If so, atomic heating might be applicable for some 10 per cent of the nation's population.

In summary, our findings suggest that in the U. S. the total cost savings from atomic power would be very small, but important changes in the structure of the economy might occur. Process changes might greatly increase the demand for power, and at the same time the availability of atomic power might reduce the market for conventional fuels. These process changes might also give rise to new industrial activities designed to meet the needs for novel types of industrial equipment, new and untried engineering skills, and so on. Atomic power would be a great stimulus to regional economic development. It would have especially important effects in regions where human resources have been underutilized in the past. The establishment of new industries in such regions would set in motion a chain reaction leading to higher per capita income in the area, primarily as a result of the effective employment of local labor. In this case the increased mobility of the fuel resource might serve, in effect, as a partial substitute for the lack of mobility of the workers who have remained in the region despite the scarcity of local opportunities for employment.

Let us turn now to the possible effects of atomic power in other countries. The U. S. is rich in conventional fuels. It seems obvious that in countries where such fuels are scarce the impact of atomic power could be much greater. But we must begin by noting an important reservation. At the present time electric power, the most likely form in which atomic energy will be made available, accounts for only a small part of any nation's total energy consumption. For example, in the U. S. no more than about 15 per cent of the total energy consumed is electricity; the rest is heat and mechanical forms of energy. If atomic power could satisfy only this fraction of a nation's total energy requirements, its importance would be severely limited. Consequently the usefulness of atomic power to countries lacking other fuels will depend on their developing process changes that will enable them to make greater use of electricity. It will be much more important to them than it is to the U. S. to find new ways to use atomic energy in the production of steel, fertilizers and construction materials like cement and brick, in railroad transportation and in the heating of homes. Assuming that they do so, however, the possibilities of atomic power may be very large indeed, for countries that have very limited supplies of conventional fuels would have a different approach to the cost of atomic power from that of the U. S., which can compare its cost closely with that of plentiful other fuels.

What are these energy-poor countries? Argentina and Brazil are prime examples: they have negligible resources of fuel, and many of their important population centers are far from potential water power. Then there are countries like Denmark and those of North Africa, which lack not only fuel but water power. Another class is represented by Hungary, which has some fuel resources but of low grade and costly to mine. Again there are countries like Italy, Austria and Switzerland which have water power but have already developed a large part of this potential and will find it increasingly difficult and expensive to expand their energy supplies further. Finally there are countries like Great Britain which have had plenty of fuel in the past but may find it increasingly difficult to mine adequate supplies in the future.

Fuel-short countries can, of course, import fuel from countries that possess sufficient supplies; Brazil and Argentina have imported coal from Great Britain across thousands of miles of ocean.

But the difficulty of acquiring foreign exchange may impose limitations on a country's ability to pay for very large amounts of fuel from abroad. Consider Brazil, for example. That country's population before World War II was about 45 million. Its total consumption of coal was about 2.5 million tons a year. On the other hand, Great Britain, with a population of about 48 million, only a little larger than Brazil's, consumed about 200 million tons of coal per year. If Brazil were to consume only one fourth as much coal per capita as the British did before the war, it would need to import approximately 45 million tons annually—some 30 times as much as it actually imported in 1939. At $8 per ton, the approximate prewar price, this level of imports would cost about $360 million, which is about $50 million more than the total value of Brazil's imports of all commodities in 1939. Such a volume of coal imports could not be financed without a radical change in Brazil's foreign trade position.

Now if atomic fuel, instead of coal, oil or water power, becomes the basis of power, the picture changes radically. The international distribution of uranium and thorium is probably quite different from that of other energy resources. Brazil, which is deficient in mineral fuels, has extensive resources of thorium. So has India, a nation with poorly distributed resources of conventional fuels.

Even more important is the fact that it will be immensely cheaper to import uranium or thorium than coal or oil. As we have seen, a pound of uranium would be equivalent in energy to 1,250 tons of coal. On that basis it would cost Brazil only $1 million to import uranium with energy equivalent to $360 million worth of coal.

This saving in the cost of fuel would not necessarily be the net saving for atomic power, since the saving of foreign exchange would also depend on how much of the plant facilities for nuclear reactors could be produced within the country. An underdeveloped country, for example, probably would have to import most of the special equipment required, perhaps for decades. Our analysis shows that despite this, the so-called backward countries might achieve substantial savings in foreign exchange by using nuclear fuel instead of coal. For an advanced country such as Great Britain the advantage would be much greater, because Britain could be expected to build and equip its own atomic energy plants.

In considering the possibilities for development of atomic power in backward countries we must give considerable weight to the capital investment required. It seems altogether probable that the investment for the construction of an atomic power plant will be substantially higher than for a conventional coal-burning plant. Since the backward areas generally have a shortage of capital, and hence have relatively high interest rates, this would be a serious drawback. But our analysis suggests that in some regions of the world the over-all investment for an industrial system based on atomic power might be no greater, and perhaps smaller, than for one based on conventional fuels. A coal-based economy would require an enormous investment in coal mines, coal-carrying railroads and so on. Hydroelectric power also demands a large capital investment.

We reached the general conclusion that in countries poor in conventional energy resources the foreign exchange advantages might weigh heavily in favor of atomic power, while in backward countries that have ample conventional sources of energy the scarcity of capital and consequent high interest rates might favor ordinary power. In this connection the history of hydroelectric power development may be significant. Despite the fact that hydroelectric projects require a heavier investment than plants using mineral fuels, even underdeveloped regions have frequently found it worth while to build them. A major reason offered for this decision is the saving achieved in foreign exchange which would otherwise have to be spent for importing fuel.

When it comes to individual industries, there are some substantial differences in the prospects of atomic power in the U. S. and in other countries. For example, we found that in the U. S. the use of nuclear energy for powering railroads is very unlikely. In the first place a nuclear engine for locomotives seems impractical. In view of the shielding required for the reactor, it appears improbable that the locomotive could be made small enough to travel on present tracks or clear present tunnels, bridges, railroad terminals and so on. Moreover, it may be uneconomic to build a reactor engine with the relatively small power output that a locomotive uses.

Consequently if atomic power is used by railroads at all, it will probably be applied to electrification of the roads from central power stations. In the U. S. the average density of traffic in most regions is not sufficient to justify general electrification even at the minimum estimated cost of atomic power. A further obstacle is that if atomic power were produced at this cost, it would probably replace coal for many other uses, which in turn would reduce coal shipments and perhaps cut rail traffic below the minimum necessary to justify electrification. On the whole, the most likely trend in the U. S. is toward the use of Diesel oil rather than coal or nuclear energy for railroads.

On the other hand, some of the countries that lack mineral fuels may very well find the use of atomic power for railroads preferable to importing fuel. They might find it to their advantage to electrify their main lines and use coal or oil for subsidiary ones. In Switzerland more than 80 per cent of the rail traffic before the war was carried on electrified lines, based on water power, and in Sweden 40 per cent of the railroad mileage was electrified; in Italy, 10 per cent.

There are similar national differences in the possibilities for the use of atomic power in steelmaking. Great Britain, whose coking coal reserves are limited, probably would apply atomic power to its steel industry before the U. S. In less developed countries, which today produce little or no steel, the possibilities would be even more attractive. As these countries industrialize, they will need great amounts of steel for factories, machines, railroads and so forth. To countries such as India and Brazil, which possess vast iron-ore reserves but comparatively little coking coal, the hydrogen reduction process based on atomic electricity may seem the best answer to the problem of building a large-scale steel industry. On the whole it is reasonable to believe that the new metallurgy opened up by atomic power might provide one of the most promising methods for expanding steel output in underdeveloped areas.

Our study gave some attention to the problem of the role that atomic power might play in the general industrialization of backward areas. It is clear at once that the availability of energy is not itself the decisive factor. The most important requirement is capital, and the scarcity of capital in those parts of the world is probably a more serious obstacle to future industrialization than a shortage of energy. But virtually all the important underdeveloped areas are proposing and undertaking planned industrialization. If atomic power becomes feasible and available to them, thereby removing at least the energy limitation, it is likely to play an extremely important part in their industrialization.

Which countries would it help most? Surprising as it may seem, China is one of the least likely to find any advantage in atomic power. It has abundant coal, well distributed throughout the country. Its iron ore resources are comparatively small. However, ubiquitous atomic power might enable it to substitute light metals for iron and steel and thus facilitate industrialization; atomic power might also help it to develop local industries in the remote interior.

Japan is perhaps a more promising region for atomic development. It has considerable hydroelectric power, but it is already pressing upon the limits of its energy resources, and atomic reactors would provide a very welcome new source of power.

India has some coal and large possibilities for hydroelectric development, but the latter are likely to be expensive in that country, and atomic power at the lower estimated costs might be competitive. India also suffers from a shortage of coking coal, so the hydrogen reduction process for iron might favor atomic power. The area of the world to which atomic power might hold out the most promise is South America. That continent is almost entirely lacking in coal, and its water power is relatively inaccessible. On the other hand, it has many of the other requirements for industrialization—with the important exception of capital.

As might be expected, one of the most striking aspects that emerges from an analysis of the possibility of ubiquitous, low-cost power is the great influence it is likely to have in promoting regional development. For the backward countries, starting from scratch, atomic power may make it possible to choose whether to concentrate their future industries in a few areas or disperse them widely, placing them in close contact with agriculture. The larger underdeveloped countries may well decide to begin modestly by building regional economies in which local industries will process local agricultural products for consumption and manufacture the tools, machinery and fertilizer needed by agriculture. This approach has influenced many of the plans for industrialization and for "valley authorities" in those countries.

The development of industry in close proximity to agriculture might reduce population migrations, provide off-season factory work for farmers and farm labor, ease the transition of the displaced handicraft worker to the new economy, facilitate the mechanization of farming and accelerate the acculturation of the predominantly agricultural population to an industrialized society.

THE ATOMIC ENERGY ACT OF 1954

by David F. Cavers

EIGHT YEARS AGO a great debate came to a close with the adoption of the Atomic Energy Act of 1946. The Act created what James R. Newman, one of its draftsmen, later termed "an island of socialism in a sea of private enterprise." It turned over to the civilian Atomic Energy Commission a monopoly of the production and ownership of fissionable materials. Only research and development in nuclear energy escaped its complete control, and even this opening for private exploitation of the atom was limited by a ban on patents except for nonmilitary uses of fissionables—and then subject to compulsory licensing.

In the long and stormy recent Senate debate over revision of the 1946 Act and adoption of the Atomic Energy Act of 1954, this "island of socialism" was the center of the controversy. Rising against a revision which they called a $12-billion atomic giveaway, a little band of senators talked on through the summer days and nights, wresting concessions now and then from the exasperated majority. But neither the public nor even the scientists who had fought for the original Act came to their aid. The efforts of Representative Chet Holifield, of the Joint Congressional Committee, to sharpen the issues and arouse public opinion had evoked little response. Civilian control of atomic energy was no longer at issue. Scientists had become discouraged about the possibilities of regaining freedom of information—domestic and international—during the twelve years of tight governmental monopoly. There was an inviting chance that a wider scope for private enterprise would bring with it greater freedom for science.

Be that as it may, pressures had long been building up for a change in the basic policies of the 1946 Act. How the Congress responded in the 1954 Act this chapter will seek to examine, in the light of the issues raised.

Perhaps the initial impetus to the drive for revision came from the "industrial participation program" begun in 1951 by the AEC in co-operation with four industrial groups who wished to look into the economic feasibility of atomic power. These groups, originally comprising eight electric utility and chemical companies, grew steadily in membership and later in number. Meanwhile forecasts of reactors competitive with conventional power plants were cropping up in the press, and atomic power began to capture the public imagination.

The final official stimulus to revision came when, last February, President Eisenhower recommended to the Congress the Act's amendment for three purposes: "widened co-operation with our allies," "improved procedures" for the handling of information and "broadened participation in the development of peacetime uses of atomic energy." After hearings before the Joint Congressional Committee on Atomic Energy, a comprehensive measure rewriting the law was reported out to both Houses on July 12.

The bill might have been passed with less debate than actually developed had there not arisen an issue which focused attention on the Administration's general power policy. This issue was posed by the so-called Dixon-Yates contract. Because its injection into the debate gave a special cast to the consideration of the entire bill, the background of this contract must be examined.

The TVA had joined with a corporation, Electric Energy, Inc., created by five utility companies, to furnish power to the AEC's great Paducah development. Power shortages in the Memphis area had led the TVA to propose to build a steam plant at near-by Fulton, Tenn. However, the Administration is opposed to building up publicly owned power, especially steam power. An alternative proposal suddenly appeared, sponsored by two Southern utilities in the Paducah group which became known as the Dixon-Yates combination. Their plan was to create a subsidiary with $5-million capital to build a $107-million power plant at West Memphis, Ark. This would sell its power on a contract of 25 to 35 years to the AEC, which in turn would resell to TVA, the latter lacking legal power to commit itself for a 25-year period.

Democrats, led by Senator Albert Gore of Tennessee, attacked the Dixon-Yates contract as going beyond AEC's contractual powers and as putting the AEC in the power business in "an awkward and unbusinesslike way," to quote Henry D. Smyth, one of the three AEC Commissioners who acquiesced in the plan only after a Presidential directive. The objectors declared that the contract would cost the Government $3,685,000 more per year than the proposed TVA plant, and they offered it as evidence of the lengths to which the Administration would go to cripple TVA and subvert public power.

Although the question about the AEC's authority to enter into such a contract was disposed of by adoption of a Republican-sponsored amendment giving it that authority, the opponents did not relax their attack. They argued that the Administration was departing in the bill from the Federal power policies of the past half-century. The Senators were much more at home on this subject than on the atom itself, and they were able to bring to their aid political forces—such as REA co-operatives and the public power bodies of the West—far stronger than any lobby of scientists.

This impact forced a number of amendments and compromises in the final form of the bill. It also must inevitably guide any attempt to define the principal questions resolved by the new Atomic Energy Act.

First let us see how the Congress, in revising the law, carried out its purpose of providing for the development of an atomic power industry. The Act leaves in the hands of the AEC the exclusive ownership of all atomic fuel, renamed "special nuclear materials" to encompass fusibles as well as fissionables. However, Section 103 empowers it to issue nonexclusive licenses authorizing applicants to have "any type of utilization or production facility" that the AEC has found "sufficiently developed to be of practical value for industrial or commercial purposes." Such licensees can then apply for a license to obtain source materials or special nuclear materials upon the payment of a "reasonable charge." (Of course, all licensees must observe conditions specified for public health and safety and the common defense and security.) The AEC retains title to the special nuclear materials it has distributed, even though these may in time be transmuted beyond recall. Further, the AEC automatically acquires title to any special materials, such as plutonium, produced in private reactors. In sum, the Commission becomes by law the producer's sole customer. The producer must receive a "fair price" for the plutonium or other nuclear material manufactured. As for the electricity he may produce in his power reactor, the Act leaves to existing public authorities regulation of the prices at which he may sell it to consumers.

For the immediate future, until the AEC finds that atomic power plants have attained commercial value, it may issue licenses for private research looking toward power development.

Such is the legal position of the private atomic power industry. The first major question is: Does the Act safeguard the national interest in public power? This was the focal point of the fiercest battles and the hardest-won compromises. As the Act now stands, the AEC itself is specifically forbidden to produce commercial power. But it is authorized to sell "by-product energy" (from its military production or experimental facilities) to public and private purchasers at "reasonable and nondiscriminatory prices." It is granted the right to build a large-scale "demonstration" power plant (provided Congress specifically authorizes the construction) and to sell the plant's output commercially. And it may license an authorized Government agency to produce and sell power under Section 103.

In sum, the Act leaves the door open for public power, though only in principle and without specific authorizations or grants of funds. The public-power proponents also succeeded in inserting into the Act the traditional "preference clauses" that give public agencies and co-operatives preference in the purchase of government-generated power. In this case the same preference is also given to regions where electricity is costly. The preference clauses relate to by-product power and the issuance of licenses under Section 103 when there are more bidders than available licenses. How significant these clauses will be is hard to tell. The AEC is not required to locate its plants in areas where public power-using agencies or co-operatives flourish or where power costs are high. It may instead be enticed by attractive terms to build a plant in a location where it may serve a large utility.

A second major question is: Will private atomic power be fairly and effectively regulated?

Under the Federal Power Act private hydroelectric projects are licensed for a 50-year period, at the end of which the Government may retake them upon reimbursing the remaining net investment. No such recapture is provided for private atomic power installations. Congress can justly argue that the water-power and atomic-power situations are different. A dam site represents a unique location; its possession by one private interest precludes its development by others. Atomic power plants, in contrast, can multiply in response to need. Recapture of these plants seems a needless precaution, especially since the Government is authorized to retake them in case of national emergency upon payment of just compensation.

Of greater concern is the question as to how the AEC is to decide what is a "reasonable charge" for the atomic fuel it sells to licensees, and what is a "fair price" for the fissionable products it buys from them. The Act gives relatively little guidance on these points. In setting its "reasonable charge" for fuel the AEC is directed to take its production costs into account, but if the average "fair price" paid to private producers for the same material is lower than its own production costs, it must sell at the lower figure. The standard for "fair price" is even more nebulous. The AEC is directed to consider production costs and the value of the purchased material for the use to be made of it. Certainly the value of, say, plutonium for bomb purposes is hard to gauge. If the plutonium is acquired with a view to resale, the "fair price" would seem to depend on the "reasonable charge," but this may depend on "fair price." Furthermore, the "fair price" must be uniform to all producers; will the higher-cost producers consider a price "fair" if it fails to cover their production costs? Covering them may push the "fair price" paid by the AEC to a level well above its own production cost. In that case the AEC may have to sell fissionables at a low price and buy them at a higher one, thus subsidizing the industry, especially the lower-cost producers who would need it least. To cap the matter, the AEC is authorized to commit itself to paying a fixed, guaranteed price for a period up to seven years ahead.

In the Congressional debate no one objected to the major source of this difficulty: the fact that the Government must hold title to all special nuclear materials and thus take all the material produced by private operators. This Government monopoly is not dictated by any Constitutional or international control consideration. Yet it will prevent the U. S. economy from benefiting fully from the creation of a private atomic industry. The impact of the efficient producers will be blunted by the Act's price-setting standards. Moreover, producers will lack incentive to open new markets for fissionables by cutting prices. If a subsidy is necessary, surely a better one could be devised.

Government ownership of fissionables gives rise to another concern. Suppose the AEC licenses a number of dual-purpose reactors providing both plutonium and electric power. What will it do if and when the U. S. decides that it has enough atomic weapons? The private reactors will still go on producing plutonium, and title to every gram they produce will promptly pop into the Government, carrying with it the duty to pay a "fair price." No doubt if the market for plutonium were glutted the AEC would stop issuing new licenses, and it might stop the output of surplus plutonium by an existing licensee by denying it new fissionables. But this would be a death sentence for the licensee. Can industry take this risk?

A third major question about the new Act is: Do the patent provisions provide adequate incentives and safeguards? The Act allows an inventor to patent his invention or discovery (save for military uses), but it requires him to license the invention to the AEC and others if it is of "primary importance" in the "production or utilization of special nuclear material for atomic energy," if the patent is of "primary importance" to the activities of the applicant and if his activities are of "primary importance" to the effectuation of the Act. The AEC may order a reluctant patentee to license an applicant at a reasonable royalty, provided the applicant can prove his case fulfills the three requirements. Obviously the hurdles the applicant must clear will deter recourse to such appeals for compulsory licensing. Probably it will remain a tool to aid in bargaining save in exceptional cases where the interests at stake are great. It may also induce many inventors to seek "awards" from the AEC instead of patents.

Yet even this well-hedged clause alarmed the Joint Committee's chairman, Representative W. Sterling Cole, Republican, of New York. He declared that the compulsory licensing provision was unconstitutional, arguing that, since the Constitution gives to the Congress the power to grant an "exclusive right" to inventors, Congress cannot make any lesser grant (a contention of dubious legal validity). Cole did not succeed in eliminating compulsory licensing from the final Act, but he did manage to include a provision of his own giving the Government the patent on any invention made under any contract or other relationship with the AEC, unless the inventor could prove that he had conceived the invention independently. One trouble with this is the difficulty of proving a negative, as the applicant must often do to rebut the presumption that the invention was conceived because of connection with the AEC. The big companies wishing to take advantage of their new freedom under the new Act are also companies which have been active as AEC contractors and presumably will continue to be so for many years. It is hard to see how their employees will be able to prove that they have not at some time come into contact with AEC work which may have inspired their inventions. Indeed, Cole's provision may prove much more depressing to private invention than the compulsory licensing provisions.

The Act, as the President recommended, limits the period during which new patents are subject to compulsory licensing to the next five years. It should be noted that compulsory licensing will apply to patents issued during that period throughout their 17-year lifetime and not merely for the five years. Whether the next five years will be the period of most important invention is, of course, unknown; the five years following may be still more active, especially if many companies stop doing contract work for the AEC.

In gauging the significance of the patent problem, one must give due weight to the fact that the discoveries will fall principally in the domain of the equipment manufacturers, not of the power companies. Probably the pressure to reduce the cost of atomic power to a level competitive with conventional fuels will deter excessive charges for equipment. There may even be a pooling of patents of the sort that was so helpful in launching the automobile industry.

The atomic patents situation is likely to remain clouded for the next five years.

A fourth major question about the Act is: Does it adequately fulfill its purpose of promoting international co-operation in the development and use of atomic energy?

The 1946 Act blocked the disclosure of restricted atomic information to other nations, however friendly. The atomic bomb was our "secret," and we were taking no chances with it—except the chances involved in failing to give to an ally military information essential to effective co-operation. In time the self-defeating character of rigid restraints became clear. In 1951 the Congress edged closer to co-operation in military matters by a tightly drafted amendment authorizing some disclosure of restricted data to friendly nations.

The new Act goes further. It authorizes the President to make agreements for co-operation with other nations or regional defense organizations. The agreements do not require Congressional approval, though they must be submitted to the Joint Committee for its information thirty days in advance. The Government may export source and by-product materials, fissionables and production and utilization facilities. However, there are precautions and restrictions aplenty. Besides the President, the AEC and (on military matters) the Defense Department must give assurances that the co-operation is in the interests of the U. S.; the co-operating nations must guarantee not to divert materials granted for peaceful uses to military purposes, and they must contract to observe strict security safeguards.

The authority to transmit nonmilitary information is wide, but disclosures of military data are limited to those which will not "reveal important information concerning the design or fabrication of the nuclear components of an atomic weapon." Our allies may be told only the weapons' external characteristics, energy yields, effects and methods of delivery.

There was no debate on these provisions. But the President's atomic pool plan seemed to present a greater hazard; the pool might have United Nations sponsorship and the Soviet Union might join as a co-operator. Facing this contingency, the Congress required that any plan for pooling material and work in the non-military applications of atomic energy among a group of nations must be authorized by "an international arrangement"—defined as a treaty or an agreement approved by both Houses.

Senator John O. Pastore of the Joint Committee sought to limit the safeguards in the case of a pool to the same ones provided for binational co-operation, but his amendment was tabled by a 46 to 41 vote, leaving for future discussion whether the Congress may constitutionally condition in this manner the President's freedom to enter into executive agreements with other nations.

The chairmanship of the AEC was another issue in the debate. The Joint Committee hearings on the bill had brought into the open suspicions that, under the chairmanship of Admiral Lewis L. Strauss, the AEC was not a happy family. After hearing testimony from three of the Commissioners concerning the tendency for authority to centralize in the Chairman, the Committee discarded a proposal to designate the chairman as "principal officer" of the Commission and designated him instead as "official spokesman," charged with seeing to the execution of the Commission's decisions and reporting to the Joint Committee from time to time. Representative Holifield, in dissenting from the Committee report, characterized this provision as "either redundant or a roundabout way of granting him [the chairman] the additional authority he seeks."

Perhaps this is a problem that legislation cannot solve. The Chairman's temperament may be more consequential than the statutory description of the hat he wears. A chairman may be a good executive and yet lack the nice ability to draw effectively on the collective wisdom of his peers.

Behind all the argument over the Act lurked a big undebated issue: secrecy. Many have complained that the secrecy of atomic operations has impeded both the advancement of scientific knowledge and the creation of an informed public opinion. These critics had no aggressive spokesman in the Congress. Indeed, in the new Act the Congress imposed a sweeping new criminal sanction: a fine of $2,500 on any past or present employee of the AEC, other government agency, contractor or licensee, or any member of the Armed Forces, who communicates restricted data to unauthorized persons. It must be shown that the defendant knew, or had reason to believe, that the data were restricted and the recipient unauthorized, but even so the provision is scarcely a stimulus to free discussion, blanketing as it does virtually everyone who has ever known a classified fact.

The Act calls for a "continuous review" by the AEC of material that may be declassified "without undue risk" and encourages such action. Happily it also allows the AEC to prescribe clearance investigations of personnel according to the work to be done and the significance of the restricted data involved. Sensible use of this measure will reduce needless barriers of delay and inconvenience to scientific work. Moreover, the new Act's general thrust toward wider participation by industry and other countries may embolden the AEC to move more rapidly toward restoring nuclear knowledge to the public domain. Much depends on whether the law is administered reasonably or overcautiously.

As the 1954 Act emerges from the clouds of debate, one can still see part of the atomic "island of socialism" in the Federal archipelago—along with the Army, Navy, Air Force and Post Office. And the part of the island that has subsided does not leave clear sailing for private enterprise. An industry to which entry is by government permit, which requires government authority to construct its plants and acquire its raw material and fuel, which can sell its nuclear products only to the government and its radioactive byproducts only to government licensees, which is subject to regulation of the price it may charge for its power output, which must license its main inventions and employ only licensed operators, is a far cry from the world of Adam Smith. It presents a mixed economy, perhaps a mixed-up one. What we have in the 1954 Act is an experiment which was rather hastily designed but which, fortunately, can be tested and restudied without putting major values in jeopardy. I look forward to the Atomic Energy Act Amendments of 1959.

INTERNATIONAL CO-OPERATION

by Donald J. Hughes

JANUARY 17, 1955, was a historic day in the Atomic Age. On that morning the submarine *Nautilus* glided into Long Island Sound under nuclear power, launching the world's first use of atomic power for transport. On that same Monday morning scientists of several countries met at the United Nations to lay plans for the world's first international conference on development of atomic energy for peaceful purposes. And the same morning the U.S.S.R. announced a program for nuclear power collaboration among nations within the Communist orbit.

These three events within a single day demonstrated how rapidly things are moving in the atomic power field, politically as well as technologically. Twelve years after the first successful chain reaction in Chicago, giving birth to the nuclear era, the large-scale gains to man so eagerly prophesied at the time are beginning to emerge. The first nuclear power furnaces are already functioning. Almost every important nation in the world is engaged, in greater or lesser degree, in exploring nuclear power. And now that President Eisenhower's "atomic pool" proposal has broken the ice for international co-operation, the pace should accelerate. Soon a number of nations will be sharing information on nuclear power, and probably fissionable material also. It may well be that between the West and the East there will be competition rather than co-operation in the race to make nuclear power economically feasible, but the ultimate effect of such a competition is likely to be all to the good.

At the international conference under the auspices of the UN at Geneva last summer, some eighty nations were represented. Their scientists and technicians had much to talk about, not only reactor technology but also such matters as the availability of uranium, its cost relative to coal and so on. There was nothing of the character of a one-way affair about this meeting; the U. S. did not find itself merely passing on its knowledge to have-not nations. Some of the European nations, especially, had a great deal to contribute to us, for they have been exploring and developing ideas of their own.

As a Fulbright professor and State Department specialist in Europe last year, I had an opportunity to survey the work in atomic power in England and on the Continent. Measured in dollars, the programs of all the nations of Western Europe together do not begin to approach our own. But they are working vigorously and pushing ahead rapidly to practical application, in some respects much more rapidly than we are. In Europe most of the nuclear work is open and was shown to me freely.

The British were the first, as far as is known, to produce useful heat from a reactor. For four years now the large graphite pile at Harwell has been heating buildings at the laboratory. It is not cheap heat, but it represents nuclear power which would otherwise be thrown away, as is now done with hundreds of thousands of kilowatts at our Hanford plants. And Great Britain has made such rapid strides on the road to nuclear power that she was able to announce last month a spectacular program, contemplating the construction of twelve nuclear power plants in the next ten years.

Britain has been pushed to this effort by her coal emergency; her mines are so depleted that she has begun to import coal from the U. S. At the same time her electric power needs are rising swiftly; they have doubled in the past ten years and will double again in the next ten. The nuclear power program is an answer to this crisis. The British will spend some $840 million to build the twelve plants. They will yield 1.5 million kilowatts or more of electricity, burning some 500 or 600 tons of nuclear fuel a year instead of five or six million tons of coal. The cost of the electricity is expected to be about seven mills per kilowatt-hour—comparable to the cost at coal-burning stations. Looking ahead twenty years, the British believe that by 1975 nuclear plants may supply 15 million kilowatts, a fourth of the nation's total electric power. Replying to a member of the House of Lords who objected last year to spending six million pounds on a "grandiose scheme" for a 20,000-kilowatt nuclear power plant, Lord Salisbury, head of the atomic program, said that was just a beginning: by the year 2000 most of Britain's electricity would be generated by nuclear fuel.

Two preliminary reactors are already under construction. At Calder Hall on the Cumberland coast the British Atomic Energy Authority is building a 40,000-kilowatt power plant costing some $50 million. Using natural uranium and graphite as the moderator, it is conventional in all respects except that the coolant will be carbon dioxide under high pressure. This plant will go into operation soon. The other experimental plant, in Scotland, will be a fast-neutron breeder, producing electricity and plutonium fuel.

The twelve large new plants will be built on a staggered schedule starting in 1957. They will include gas-cooled and liquid-cooled types, perhaps even a homogeneous reactor. Some of the plants may produce as much as 200,000 kilowatts. The British estimate that the fabricated uranium fuel for a large plant of the Calder Hall type will cost about $14 million and will have to be renewed every three to five years.

France's atomic energy effort, though on a much smaller scale than the British, is being pursued with equal seriousness. Year by year France has to import more coal, and her engineers have investigated all possible power possibilities, even the harnessing of the tides. The French will soon build a 40,000-kilowatt reactor to produce plutonium as capital for fueling breeder reactors. They now have two research reactors of the heavy-water type. One is an extremely good research instrument; its neutron flux is twice as intense as that of the reactor at our Brookhaven National Laboratory.

Norway got an early start in the nuclear power field, primarily because she possessed one of the first plants for making heavy water. The Norwegians made a co-operative arrangement with the Dutch to obtain uranium and built a 300-kilowatt research pile in Oslo four years ago. I found an international group working at this pile, including scientists from the Netherlands, France, Yugoslavia and India. Norway is now going ahead with plans for a mobile reactor for ship propulsion.

In Sweden a low-power research reactor went into operation several months ago. It is located in a large room blasted out of rock under a park in Stockholm. This reactor is being used primarily to gain experience in neutron physics. The second Swedish reactor will be a power producer.

In the Netherlands a group of scientists and engineers, having gained knowledge from the co-operative construction of the Norwegian pile, are pushing ahead on plans for a power-producing reactor. A visit to their research center at Arnhem convinced me that they are considering designs much more advanced than any discussed in the U. S. Drawing on their considerable experience in handling slurries and powders, the Dutch propose to use uranium fuel in the form of fluidized powder. If the idea is successful, they will avoid all the complicated problems of protective coatings and removal of fuel elements that apply to the usual solid-fuel reactors.

In other European countries, reactor projects were not quite so far along. Nevertheless in every country I found groups enthusiastically at work. From each I got a strong feeling that atomic energy is looked on as indispensable to the country's industrial future. The projects are tiny compared to those of the U. S., but because of that very fact the investigators feel freer to try new ideas. For example, a small group working under Werner Heisenberg in Germany is making extraordinarily dense graphite on an experimental scale. The German scientists also feel that they can develop more economical methods for making heavy water; one gets the impression that their chances of success are very good. The Italians and French are working on the same problem.

What I saw in western Europe is but a sample of the worldwide interest and activity in peacetime nuclear power. India, for example, has just arranged to buy ten tons of heavy water from the U. S. Atomic Energy Commission for a research reactor to be built near Bombay. Australia, New Zealand, the Philippines, Formosa, Pakistan, Iran, Turkey, Greece and Spain are among the other countries starting work in atomic energy.

If Europe's scientists are making such rapid progress, why are they so enthusiastic about the international atomic pool and help from the U. S.? What have we to give them? The answer is: mainly detailed technical knowledge. We have a great wealth of information on reactor building and operation (e.g., the behavior of materials at high temperature and under intense radiation) which can save the other nations years of expensive research and testing. Communication of the results of our research can solve many of their problems with very little effort on our part.

Our atomic energy program has been so vast, and so hedged with secrecy, that the Europeans tend to suppose that we have explored all avenues to nuclear power and that ideas we are not pursuing have been proved unworkable. The truth is that our program, preoccupied with production of fissionables, has necessarily been conservative. We have not investigated all avenues. The Europeans are in an excellent position to try novel approaches which will repay us for the engineering help we give them.

Of course most of these nations also need fissionable material. Nuclear fuel is the capital one must have to start in the atomic energy business. To obtain this capital each nation would have to build, at enormous cost, large plants for separating uranium 235 or making plutonium. But with a gift or loan of fuel from us, other countries could pay back the original outlay of fissionables within a few years.

Coupled with the great enthusiasm for the U. S. pool plan, I found in every country a certain amount of skepticism. In the months following President Eisenhower's proposal, months in which apparently nothing happened, the Europeans came to look upon it as mere propaganda. However, when it became known that private negotiations with the U.S.S.R. had been going on during this period, the European scientists became much more impressed by the serious intent of the U. S. Now that steps toward international co-operation have at last begun, their optimism and spirit have revived.

What the U. S. has to gain from the proposed international agency will not be obvious at first but should become more apparent as time goes on. The European scientists are extremely good; they are moving ahead boldly and rapidly in spite of tremendous material handicaps. The rapidity with which they are mastering the atomic energy field and the thoroughgoing nature of their investigations is proof of their ability. In many laboratories I found them investigating fundamentals of neutron physics which we have never had time to study in detail. I became convinced that under the present conditions they will do much more careful work on these fundamentals of reactor physics than we shall do. With our help, in very short order they will be producing results of great value to us—results that will be doubly valuable because they are done with a fresh approach. Already the European work on such things as international neutron-source calibrations and standardizations of certain basic neutron cross sections has helped our own standardization tremendously.

In the nuclear field we shall be engaging in "trade, not aid." The trade will be an exchange of extremely valuable fundamental scientific concepts on which all the economic progress will depend. European scientists will also begin to offer competition with us in atomic energy which will have a salutary effect.

All this is independent of the part to be played by the U.S.S.R. Even if the Russians do not participate in the program, their competition will stimulate the West. If they do come in, something important may happen in international relations. During the years from 1942 to 1945, when only a few men knew of the tremendous new force that had been unleashed from the atom, they often talked of the possibility that it might become a force for peace in the postwar world. Perhaps the atom may still serve as an instrument for demonstrating that international co-operation can work.

PART 5 RADIOBIOLOGY

I. THE LETHAL EFFECTS OF RADIATION

by Edward Spoerl

There was not much interest in or concern about the problem of the lethal effects of radiation upon cells in 1940 when Edward Spoerl was completing his undergraduate work in the field of genetics at the University of Wisconsin. When he received his doctoral degree in plant physiology at Wisconsin in 1947, however, radiobiology had become an active branch of science. After two years of teaching body and plant physiology, first at the University of Wisconsin and then at the University of Arizona, Spoerl went to the Atomic Energy Commission Mound Laboratory at Miamisburg, Ohio, where he headed the Biochemistry Section and conducted research on the cellular effects of ionizing radiation. He is now Chief of the Cellular Research Section at the Army Medical Research Laboratory, Fort Knox, Kentucky.

II. TRACERS

by Martin D. Kamen

The co-discoverer of Carbon 14, the most valuable tracer isotope of all, Martin D. Kamen originally planned to concentrate in music and literature when he matriculated at the University of Chicago in 1930. A freshman course in chemistry set him on a career in the sciences, and he emerged six years later with a Ph.D. in physical chemistry. At the University of California, he teamed up with Samuel Ruben, a contemporary who was pioneering the use of radioactive tracers for biological research. Together, in 1940, they discovered Carbon 14. Their partnership was ended by the war, Kamen joining the Manhattan District and Ruben going into the laboratories of the Chemical Warfare Service, where he lost his life in a research accident. Kamen is now associate professor at Washington University, St. Louis, where his work in problems of photosynthesis and metabolism is continuing to win distinction.

THE LETHAL EFFECTS OF RADIATION

by Edward Spoerl

WHY AND HOW does radiation kill? Since 1945 U. S. biologists have focused an immense amount of study on this important question, but we are still far from any clear answer to it. Here is an invisible lethal force which attacks from the blue without being felt or sensed in any way, and over a period that may vary from days to years produces a slow death of the organism. It is clear that the breakdown and death occur at the most fundamental level of life —in the body's cells. But the process by which this happens remains a mystery. We can only speculate about possible mechanisms.

We know that some tissues of the body are much more sensitive to radiation than others. In general, cells that are dividing and reproducing rapidly are more affected than the less active ones. It is in the sites where blood cells are manufactured that radiation does its readiest damage. Most vulnerable are the lymphoid tissues—the lymph nodes, spleen, tonsils and so on—which produce and store white blood cells. Radiation destroys these factories of the white cells and breaks down the cells themselves. Since the white cells are one of the most important defenses against bacteria, this damage greatly lowers the body's resistance to infection. The bone marrow, which manufactures the red blood cells, is similarly sensitive to radiation. Also vulnerable are the sex glands, the skin (which loses its hair when exposed to heavy radiation), the linings of the gastrointestinal tract and the walls of the blood capillaries (which may be so weakened that the victim has hemorrhages throughout his body).

The first troublesome question is: By what means does radiation produce these effects on the body? Is the damage to the tissues due to direct action by the radiation (i.e., to a breakup or destruction of the cells) or to some indirect effect, such as the conversion of body substances into poisons or the release of poisons from the injured cells? There are differing schools of thought on these issues, but however the problem is approached, all roads lead eventually to investigation of what is happening in the cell. For obvious reasons most of the fundamental studies of radiation effects have been done on the simpler plants and micro-organisms.

Such studies show that radiation affects cells in various ways. It may kill the cells outright; it may interfere with their growth; it may change their genes and heredity. For instance, Cornell University investigators who studied corn seeds irradiated in the atomic bomb test at Bikini found that the seeds produced stunted plants with mottled leaves; the mottled areas consisted of dead cells and cells that were alive but colorless instead of the usual green. Under the microscope it could be seen that the heredity-carrying chromosomes in many of the cells were disrupted. The same general effects have been demonstrated in numerous experiments on bacteria and fungi: irradiation kills many of the cells, causes genetic mutations, inhibits respiration and, by stopping cell division, sometimes produces abnormally large cells.

Since the life and death of a cell ultimately depends on its metabolism, or chemistry, it is here that we must look for the basic effects of radiation. Fundamentally these effects are due to the radiation's ionizing action on the atoms and molecules of which the cell is composed. Any radiation, whether in the form of X-rays or gamma rays or particles such as neutrons or beta particles, ionizes the atoms among which it passes; that is to say, it removes an electron from a neutral atom, creating a positive ion, and the released electron then joins another atom to form a negative ion. This is not a selective process: the radiation will ionize impartially any atom or molecule in its path, whether it is water, a protein, an enzyme, a hormone or any other substance. And the ionization may change the molecule in an important way, making it a great deal more active chemically.

Now the main constituent (about 70 per cent) of most cells is water. Consequently when radiation passes through a cell, the water molecules are most likely to be ionized, simply because of their predominance in numbers. This suggests that the ionization of water may be one of the chief means, perhaps the major one, by which radiation produces its effects on cells. Such a theory is strongly supported by the known facts about the chemical behavior of water molecules when they are irradiated. It appears that radiation removes an electron from the water molecule and forms a positive H_2O ion. The H_2O^+ ion then breaks down to H^+ and OH. The free electron may become attached to another water molecule and form a negative H_2O ion, which in turn breaks into H and OH^-. These fractions may react with one another to form not only water molecules but also H_2O_2 (hydrogen peroxide) and HO_2. Furthermore, the free hydrogen can combine with oxygen in the living cell and through a series of reactions produce more HO_2 and H_2O_2. The important fact is that the ionization of water and the resulting reactions yield four powerful oxidizing agents: H_2O_2, O and the free radicals OH and HO_2. These agents can oxidize substances in a cell and thus interfere with its normal chemical reactions.

What kind of damage could they do? E. S. G. Barron of the University of Chicago, who has given this matter a good deal of study, suggests that the oxidizing agents may inactivate enzymes, thereby disturbing the cell's metabolism. Enzymes are the organic catalysts that assist or make possible the chemical reactions in cells. They are proteins. Now the enzyme protein molecule contains sulfur and hydrogen linked together in sulfhydryl groups (SH), and it is known that many enzymes cannot function if these groups are oxidized or otherwise changed. Barron believes that the oxidizing agents formed in an irradiated cell oxidize the sulfhydryl groups and thus put the enzymes out of action.

He and his co-workers have found strong experimental evidence to support this theory. For instance, they have shown that when solutions of certain simple compounds containing a sulfhydryl group are exposed to X-rays, the radiation oxidizes these compounds. In other experiments they irradiated dilute solutions of the actual enzymes, that is, enzymes requiring sulfhydryl groups for their action. They found that the various kinds of radiation they used—X-rays, alpha, beta and gamma rays—inactivated these enzymes.

Carrying the experiments a step further, they proved that the oxidation of sulfhydryl groups is reversible; i.e., the enzymes can be reactivated. For example, by adding to the solution a compound such as glutathione, which supplies sulfhydryl groups, they made inactivated enzymes function again. But this is possible only when the enzymes have received moderate doses of radiation. After a large dose the enzymes can be reactivated only partly or not at all. This indicates that the heavy dose produces some additional damage besides oxidation of the sulfhydryl groups; that it changes, or "denatures," the enzyme protein in some way. What this change may be is not yet known.

These experiments seem to support the idea that radiation damages or kills cells mainly by an indirect process. The radiation ionizes water to form oxidizing agents; the oxidizers inactivate enzymes; this in turn starves the cell. But we have no evidence that this process is the major means by which radiation attacks the living cell. Radiation may work its damage in many other ways. Perhaps it disrupts the protein directly by breaking the molecule's chemical bonds. Perhaps it kills cells by injuring or changing their nuclear material. It is believed that radiation causes the mutation of genes in the cell nucleus by some kind of direct action, perhaps by a hit on the large gene molecule. Since many mutations are lethal, this may be an important means by which cells are killed.

It is definitely known that oxygen plays an important role in the killing of cells by radiation. A recent experiment at the University of Southern California showed that rats can survive much larger doses of radiation if their oxygen supply is reduced below normal. In the biological laboratories of the Atomic Energy Commission at Oak Ridge, which is one of the principal centers of research on radiation effects, similar findings have been made: plants and fruit flies that are X-rayed in an atmosphere lacking oxygen have a much smaller percentage of chromosome aberrations and mutations than those irradiated in air. To be sure, it has not yet been proved that the effect of the oxygen is connected with the formation of oxidizing agents by the ionization of water, but the experiments at least indicate that the radiation works indirectly.

The results of such experiments suggest that mutation may be produced by an indirect chemical route rather than by the radiation's direct attack on the genes. This idea is further supported by some recent experiments at the University of Texas. Hydrogen peroxide, which as we have seen is one of the products of the ionization of water, was added to media in which bacteria were growing. Although the culture was not irradiated, mutant strains of bacteria appeared in it after a short time. The mutants were like those produced by radiation. In other words, hydrogen peroxide, a known product of radiation, is itself capable of causing mutation. Apparently it does not do so directly, because it caused cells to mutate only in a growth medium; it did not work in water. Perhaps the hydrogen peroxide reacts with organic material in the growth medium to produce organic peroxides, which, as has been proved in other experiments, are effective mutagenic agents.

There is evidence also that in its effects on the division of cells radiation operates indirectly through a chemical mechanism. It has long been known that cell division is sensitive to radiation. One striking illustration is its effect on cells of colon bacteria. These rod-shaped bacteria ordinarily are only a few microns long; they divide into daughter cells before they grow much longer than that. But a small dose of radiation, which prevents them from dividing, can cause them to grow into spaghetti-like filaments more than a hundred microns long. Now it has been observed that cells which are actively growing and dividing contain more sulfhydryl groups than do resting cells. Moreover, the addition of sulfhydryl-containing substances to the growth medium can speed up the cells' rate of division. Apparently they need these groups to assist the division process. It looks, therefore, as if radiation could stop the division of cells by oxidizing the sulfhydryl groups.

Radiation may also act on another chemical cycle involved in cell division. There is a certain acid in the nucleus of the cell—desoxypentosenucleic acid—which seems to play an important part in the division of the cell. Radiation apparently inhibits the formation of this acid, perhaps by inactivating the enzyme system that catalyzes it. The Nobel-prize chemist George Hevesy, who has studied this effect with the aid of radioactive phosphorus, has suggested that the inhibition of formation of the nucleic acid in question accounts for the selective effect of radiation on tumor cells. As is well known, radiation affects tumor cells more than it does normal cells—which is the basis for the use of X rays and radium for cancer treatment. A distinguishing characteristic of tumor cells, of course, is that they divide rapidly. They therefore need the desoxy nucleic acid, and Hevesy points out that radiation may retard the growth of a tumor by cutting off the supply of this acid. But this is only speculation; we know too little about the functions of the nucleic acids to be able to accept or reject such a theory at this stage.

From the work that has been done on radiation effects a few points seem to be reasonably clear. Oxidations evidently play an important part in radiation damage. The decomposition of water and the resultant formation of oxidizing agents may be one of the chief means by which radiation injures and kills cells. An indirect chemical mechanism could account for the various radiation effects: mutation, interference with cell division, inhibition of growth, the death of the cell. But the happenings in a cell are so complex that they are exceedingly difficult to investigate, and progress in the field of radiation effects has been slow.

One of the main reasons for devoting so much study to radiation effects, of course, is to discover ways of combatting them—a matter of some urgency in our radioactive age. So far the treatment of radiation sickness has had to be directed toward the symptoms and end results rather than toward the basic mechanism. Blood and plasma transfusions, plus the feeding of iron, vitamins and possibly amino acids, can restore the supply of blood cells and replace broken-down tissues. Antibiotics such as aureomycin can protect the weakened victim against infections. Certain substances such as protamine and toluidine blue have had some effect in stopping hemorrhage. Some cases of radiation injury have responded to the drug desoxycorticosterone acetate, presumably because this substance counteracts histamine-like poisons that may be released by radiation damage.

At a more basic level, the studies of the oxidation effects in cells suggest that a sulfhydryl-supplying substance such as glutathione may be helpful. In experiments on animals this material so far has not been effective as a treatment; it protects the animals only if it is given before they receive the dose of radiation.

Obviously the key to the whole problem lies in a better understanding of how a cell lives and functions. When that mystery has been unraveled, we may be able to cope with radiation, cancer and many of our other ills.

TRACERS

by Martin D. Kamen

THE RECENT APPLICATION of isotopes as tracers for investigating life processes is now widely recognized as one of the most significant developments in the long history of the biological sciences. The researches made possible by this technique already have yielded substantial contributions to fundamental biology. Beyond these, the visions opened by the technique have both surprised and stirred biologists. It is as if, looking into some quiet forest pool, one were to find its microscopic animal life suddenly endowed with visibility, revealing a vast activity of movement, interchange and transformation hardly indicated by the seeming calm and stability of the surface.

The power of the tracer technique is readily illustrated by a simple experiment. Suppose that a beaker is filled with a solution of sodium chloride—common table salt—in water, and the beaker is then divided into two compartments by means of a permeable membrane. Obviously material is diffusing back and forth through the membrane, yet no ordinary chemical or physical means can demonstrate this movement, for the system is in a state of equilibrium. The solution on both sides of the membrane is identical; each half of the beaker has the same number of positively-charged sodium ions and negatively-charged chlorine ions.

Now suppose some of the chloride is removed from compartment A and replaced with an equal volume of specially prepared chloride containing only the lighter isotope of chlorine—Cl^{35}, of atomic weight 35. Normal chlorine, a mixture of two stable isotopes, has an atomic weight of 35.5. Thus the new material, though chemically indistinguishable from the chloride it replaced, is lighter. In consequence the diffusion of the new chlorine ions into compartment B, as well as the rate of this diffusion, can be detected merely by observing the rate at which the weight of the solution in B decreases. Precisely the same result is obtained by labeling solution A with a radioactive, or unstable, isotope of chlorine instead of a stable one. The only difference is in the method of detection: in one case the diffusion is detected by weighing samples of the B solution, in the other by using an instrument to record radiation from the B solution.

This experiment demonstrates, at the simplest level, the principle of all tracer work. The two interacting systems, A and B, may be two pieces of solid salt—in which case the membrane is the surface of contact between them—or two pieces of metal, or a cell and its surroundings; the diffusing material may be a metal, a gas, a protein, an organic product of metabolism; the membrane may be a plant surface, an animal's skin, a cell interface. In all cases the process under study is traced by labeling one of the constituent atoms of the diffusing material with an isotope and determining its fate. When, for example, the diffusing material is a labeled hormone and the membrane a cell interface, the investigator is conducting a research into the absorption and retention of hormones by a living system.

Just as in the case of the two salt solutions, isotopic tracers can be used to distinguish material entering a cell from that already present, even though no net change in the chemical composition of the cell occurs. Thus biologists for the first time are afforded a method for investigating directly the important problem of how a cell governs the uptake of material from its environment. The great sensitivity of tracer methods also makes it possible to study the exchange of material within the cell, and the constant intercourse among the agents and products of metabolism which circulate in the organism.

Any account of the genesis of this fundamental advance, which thus far has been the most beneficial and useful fruit of nuclear science, must begin with the early nineteenth-century English physician and chemist William Prout. In 1816 he suggested that all the elements might be built of the lightest atom, hydrogen. On the Prout theory, it was expected that the atomic weight of every element would be a whole number multiple of the atomic weight of hydrogen. It turned out, however, as the weights of the elements became accurately determined, that most of them did not obey any such law. Thus chlorine, which should have had an atomic weight of 35 or 36, actually had a weight of 35.5 times hydrogen. Consequently the Prout hypothesis was abandoned. It might not have been if physicists had realized that the "irreducible" elements they measured so confidently were *mixtures* of atoms, and that the atoms themselves did follow the rule of integral atomic weights when compared with hydrogen.

The twin discoveries of X-rays and radioactivity in 1895 and 1896 changed the whole perspective. By means of new instruments capable of determining the properties of single atoms, it was soon found that most elements were actually families of atoms, the members of which, although chemically identical, differed from one another in certain physical properties, notably weight and stability. Chlorine, for example, was found to be a mixture of two types of atoms with weights of 35 and 37, present in the proportion of three to one respectively. Among the heavy elements were discovered a considerable number of radioactive varieties; thus a radioactive product of thorium called Thorium C was shown to be a member of the bismuth family, with a weight of 212 instead of 209—the weight of stable bismuth atoms. It was the British physicist-chemist Frederick Soddy, a collaborator of the great Ernest Rutherford, who in 1912 gave these variant atoms of the same element the name of isotopes, from the Greek *isos* (same) and *topos* (place), meaning that they occupied the same place in the periodic table.

Once the existence of isotopes had been discovered, chemists proceeded to attempt to separate them. The experiments they devised for this purpose naturally were based on the physical differences among isotopes that resulted from their differences in mass—such as different volatility, mobility in gases and liquids, and so on. No one was more active in this type of research than a young Hungarian chemist, George Hevesy, who had come in 1913 to Rutherford's fertile laboratory at Manchester, England. In a series of researches notable for their ingenuity and precision, Hevesy and his collaborators showed that the isolation of isotopes in noticeable quantities required the most arduous kind of laboratory procedures, involving many thousands of repeated distillations or diffusions. These observations, supported by those of other researchers, indicated that in ordinary chemical processes no appreciable differences in the isotopic composition of samples of an element would be noticed until the chemical methods for determination of atomic weight approached a precision of the order of one part in 10,000 to 100,000. Thus it was established that for all practical purposes ordinary chemical manipulations would produce no change in an element's isotopic composition.

Hevesy reasoned that if one could somehow change the isotopic composition of any sample of an element, the sample could then be distinguished from the normal element. In other words, an element could be labeled by altering its isotopic content, and the labeled material could be followed through any chemical reaction. In 1923 Hevesy made his first famous tracer experiment. Because radioactive isotopes were available only in the heavy elements, he chose to begin by studying the intake of lead by plants, and he used a radioactive isotope of lead, Thorium B, to label the material. He bathed the rootlets of young plants with solutions of lead nitrate mixed with Thorium B nitrate as the tracer. After intervals ranging from one hour to two days, he burned various parts of the plants and determined the amount of Thorium B present in each part by measuring the radioactivity of its ashes.

This experiment in plant nutrition was the beginning of the isotopic-tracer method in biology. The method was severely limited at first by the fact that all work had to be done with the heavy elements, such as lead, bismuth and mercury. No feasible method existed for the separation of stable isotopes in quantity. But the discovery of the neutron, of heavy hydrogen and of artificial radioactivity in the 1930s, and the subsequent development of large cyclotrons and atomic piles, solved these problems. By the middle 1940s there was available a practically unlimited supply of radioactive isotopes of nearly all the elements. Meanwhile Harold C. Urey and his collaborators at Columbia University, in a series of remarkable researches, developed methods for bulk separation of the stable isotopes of the important biological elements.

The assaying instruments are of two general types. In experiments using radioactive isotopes, the measuring instrument is the electroscope, the electrometer or the now familiar Geiger-Müller counter. The latter consists essentially of an ionization chamber and an electronic apparatus which perform the functions of detecting and amplifying each radioactive disintegration of an atom; the number and rate of disintegrations is a measure of the amount of labeled material present. In experiments using stable isotopes, the measuring instrument most commonly used is the mass spectrometer, which ionizes the atoms in a sample, swings them through a magnetic field and separates the isotopes by means of their differing masses. Thus the atoms of each isotope are deposited at a separate point on a collecting plate and the concentration of the labeling isotope in the sample determined.

The biochemist's use of tracers is focused primarily on this basic problem: How does a given molecule play its part in the metabolism of a living organism? More specifically, what is the mechanism by which the molecule is mobilized either as a source of energy or as a contributor to the structure of living cells? In the investigation of this problem, some of the outstanding contributors have been the late Rudolph Schoenheimer and David Rittenberg of Columbia University, Harland G. Wood of Western Reserve University, and Vincent du Vigneaud of Cornell University. Their principal tools have been the stable isotopes hydrogen 2, carbon 13 and nitrogen 15.

The result of these researches may be summed up in the important general finding that a living system is a finely balanced complex of chemical reactions which, like the salt solution in the beaker, is in a continual state of flux. Metabolism is not a simple, one-way process. The substances of cells are constantly being built up and broken down from a "metabolic pool" of chemically active fragments of molecules that circulate in the organism. Schoenheimer aptly likened the adult organism to a military regiment:

"[It has] a size which fluctuates only within . . . limits, and a well-defined, highly organized structure. The individuals of which it is composed are continually changing. Men join up, are broken, and ultimately leave after varying lengths of service. The incoming and outgoing streams of men are numerically equal, but they differ in composition. . . . Recruits may be likened to the diet; their retirement and death correspond to excretion."

This analogy is admittedly incomplete; it fails, for example, to depict the chemical interaction of body constituents in the living system. Yet it remains an admirable illustration of the meaning of the "dynamic state" in biology.

The tracing of a metabolic process, as already indicated, involves two basic steps: 1) labeling a food or another substance fed to the organism, and 2) analyzing the intermediate and ultimate products that may be formed from this substance to determine the amount, if any, of the tracer isotope present. In biological research it is sometimes preferable to use a stable isotope rather than a radioactive one, to avoid the danger of damaging the organism by radiation effects.

The labeling process itself is merely a matter of chemical preparation. The compound to be fed to the organism is synthesized chemically in the usual way; the only difference is that for one of the components in the molecule a single isotope, or an unusual proportion of that isotope, is used instead of the natural element. Thus if the atom to be labeled is nitrogen, the compound is prepared with nitrogen 15. Supplies of separated isotopes are now available commercially or from an institutional laboratory.

The tracing of the labeled material, however, is somewhat less simple than a game of hare and hounds. The labeled compound must be prepared in such a way that the label is not lost, either because of excessive dilution in the pool of the same material that is already present in the organism, or because of interference by biochemical processes not connected with the one being studied. Moreover, the success of the experiment often depends on an accurate estimate of how thoroughly the labeled compound mixes with the same material in the organism; if the mixing is incomplete, it becomes difficult to judge the significance of the concentration of labeled material finally found in the cells where it is used. A further difficulty enters with regard to the purity of the sample; in tracing the intermediate steps in metabolism it is usually no simple problem to isolate the molecules carrying the label in a state that is sufficiently pure to permit an unambiguous analysis of the meaning of their labeled content.

An outstanding example of this type of research was a series of experiments conducted by David Shemin and David Rittenberg at Columbia University. They were studying the manufacture of hemin by the human body. Hemin is the iron-containing blood pigment that combines with globin, a protein, to form hemoglobin, the substance that transports oxygen in the blood. The researchers had established that in the rat the nitrogen of hemin is derived mainly from the amino acid glycine (NH_2CH_2COOH). To trace the process in a human subject, they labeled glycine with nitrogen 15 and fed small amounts of the compound (a total of one and one-half ounces) to the subject for three days. Then at regular intervals they obtained from the subject samples of a hemin derivative called protoporphyrin and examined it for evidence of the tracer nitrogen.

Now the result one would normally have expected, in view of what was known about the dynamics of metabolism in general, is somewhat as follows: The labeled glycine would mix with the glycine already present in the circulation and within a relatively short time would become available for incorporation into the new hemin constantly being produced in the body. As new red cells were formed, labeled hemin would appear in the circulating blood. Meanwhile, unlabeled hemin would be removed from the blood as older red cells were destroyed. Thus the proportion of labeled hemin in the blood would increase steadily as long as labeled glycine was fed. Shortly after the subject returned to a normal diet containing unlabeled glycine, the situation would be reversed. Now unlabeled nitrogen would be coming into the hemin and labeled nitrogen would be going out. If the red cells were constantly exchanging material with their surroundings—a condition characteristic of practically all metabolic processes—the proportion of labeled hemin would soon start to drop. The curve recording the abundance of labeled hemin in the blood during the course of the experiment would follow a certain familiar pattern: it should rise sharply at first, level off for a brief period, and then decline.

The actual result was quite different. After the feeding of labeled glycine was stopped on the third day, the concentration of labeled hemin did not level off but continued to increase for nearly twenty-five days! Then it became stabilized for a long period. Not until the hundredth day did the concentration begin to drop.

The deduction to be drawn from these facts was clear. It appeared that hemin, unlike other active tissue, was comparatively stable. Instead of being continually broken down and rebuilt, red cells, like human beings, evidently have a definite average lifetime during which they remain intact. Normally they are destroyed or die only after reaching a certain age. The observations indicated that the average human red cell has a life span of about 130 days. The new red cells that were formed while labeled glycine was available retained the label until they died, and the labeled nitrogen then released was not used again in the manufacture of hemin.

Obviously this finding has considerable significance to medical science. Tracer nitrogen can be used to study the life span and destruction of hemin and red cells in various types of human blood disorders. Such researches have already begun and they have a bright future.

It must not be supposed that precursor-product researches are the most important type of investigation accessible to tracer techniques. They are only one aspect of the central problem in biochemistry: the elucidation of the mechanisms by which the body regulates and integrates its constant breakdown and synthesis of materials. In any given biochemical process, an important role is played by linked chains of reacting agents which act as intermediates in accepting and passing along certain necessary atomic fragments supplied by material taken into the body. Each step in such a process is controlled in general by an enzyme. All enzymes appear to be proteins. The entire process is self-contained and self-regenerating: it proceeds in a cyclic fashion. The tracer approach is particularly useful in ferreting out possible intermediates and participating molecules that are not obviously involved or are not observable by conventional chemical methods alone.

The great subtlety of the tracer approach is well illustrated by still another technique. Sometimes the biochemical product being studied does not exist in the organism in sufficient quantity to be isolated or analyzed. In such cases some of the product is added to the labeled precursor when the latter is fed to an organism. This unlabeled "carrier" material adds to the body's supply of the product; it is fed in a quantity sufficient to permit analysis of the product, but not too great to dilute the label beyond detection.

The mixing of labeled with unlabeled material is extremely useful in analytical biochemistry. Suppose, for example, one desires to ascertain whether a given compound is present in a cell extract; let us say the problem is to determine the percentage of glycine present in a mixture obtained by hydrolysis (breakdown by water) of a cell protein. This is a formidable problem by conventional chemical methods, for complete recovery of the glycine in a pure state is required and amino acids are not easy to separate from one another.

The tracer method solves it easily. We add to the extract a carefully measured quantity of labeled glycine. The labeled sample mixes with the glycine in the extract. Now we can measure the amount of glycine originally present by measuring the dilution of the label, which depends only on the relative amounts of the original glycine and the labeled addition. Suppose, for example, we add 10 milligrams of glycine containing 10 units of labeled carbon to one gram of the original protein containing an unknown amount of glycine. We now isolate and purify a small sample, say one milligram, of the mixture of labeled and unlabeled glycine, and measure the concentration of labeled carbon in it. We find that the concentration is one half of one unit. In the labeled glycine that was added the concentration was one unit per milligram. Thus it is clear that the added glycine doubled the amount originally present, which means that the extract contained 10 milligrams of glycine. Here, then, is a method of analyzing any compound for one of its components without separating out all of the component in a pure state: we need only measure the labeled content of a known amount of added material and the labeled content of a purified sample of the combined mixture; a simple formula then gives the amount of the component being measured. This method is being developed with many variations as one of the most useful analytical tests in biochemistry.

These examples suggest, but by no means completely define, the immense new frontiers opened by the isotopes in biochemistry. And biochemistry is only one of the fields of application for tracers. Their usefulness is equally impressive in physiology. An inquiry in which tracers have been especially helpful is the investigation of the biological role of elements that living cells use in vanishingly small amounts, such as boron, molybdenum, manganese, copper, and so on. The functions of these elements have been little understood, for biologists have lacked reliable techniques for studying them. By the use of labeled samples which make it possible to detect microscopic amounts of these materials, research workers have now begun to develop considerable data on their absorption, retention and excretion by the organism.

In medicine, the application of the tracer method is still only in its infancy, but much has already been done. The use of radioactive isotopes in treating certain blood disorders and some cancers is now routine. Radioactive phosphate has been shown to have definite advantages over X-rays in the treatment of polycythemia vera, a disease of the red blood cells, and of some types of leukemia, the cancer-like blood disorder. Radio-iodine is becoming a popular prescription for the control of hyperthyroidism.

In medical research, tracer studies have already made several invaluable contributions. Investigations with tracer iron of the conditions for survival of human red cells have improved the method of storing blood for transfusions. Tracers have made possible accurate measurements of the blood volume in the body under a variety of conditions, ranging from the normal condition to that of patients in extreme shock. They have permitted studies of disturbances in iron physiology that attend pregnancy. They have shed light on the dynamics of inflammation; tracers may even make it possible to locate internal sites of inflammation in the circulatory system without recourse to surgery. Labeled sodium has been used to diagnose disturbances of circulation in the small peripheral blood vessels, and to test the value of various drugs used to dilate or open the vessels.

Valuable as these direct medical harvests are, it seems clear that the most profound results of tracer research in the coming years will be achieved at the fundamental level of biochemistry and physiology. Even the most cautious observers agree that this research promises incalculable benefits to mankind.

PART 6 THERMONUCLEAR REACTIONS

I. THE HYDROGEN BOMB I*
by Louis N. Ridenour

During the war, Louis N. Ridenour was assistant director of the Radiation Laboratory at Massachusetts Institute of Technology, the center for the development of radar. As a physicist who had not been engaged in the development of the A-bomb and had not had access to classified information surrounding it, he took a leading role in the first efforts to acquaint the public with the underlying concepts and information. The present chapter on the H-bomb is similarly based upon a physicist's comprehension of the fundamentals which have been in the public domain even longer than the physics of uranium fission. When he wrote this chapter, Ridenour was dean of sciences at the University of Illinois; he has since served a term as chief scientist of the U. S. Air Force and is now in industry, working on missile systems at Lockheed Aircraft Corporation.

II. THE HYDROGEN BOMB II*
by Hans A. Bethe

Hans Bethe attained world eminence in physics in the early 1930s for his work on the thermonuclear reactions that account for the energy output of the stars. He did not then anticipate that these cosmic processes would be demonstrated on earth during his lifetime. The fusion of hydrogen atoms requires temperatures in the tens of millions of degrees. The H-bomb was not thinkable until the accidental discovery of the opposite process of uranium fission made the A-bomb a reality. During the war, Bethe made primary contributions to the A-bomb development as director of the theoretical physics section at Los Alamos. In the period since he wrote this chapter, he has made equally significant contributions to the successful achievement of the H-bomb. He left his native Germany in 1933 and has been professor of physics at Cornell since 1937.

* These two chapters were first published in SCIENTIFIC AMERICAN early in 1950 and were among the principal contributions by thoughtful scientists to public discussion at that time of the question whether the United States should proceed with the development of the H-bomb. The H-bombs subsequently developed and demonstrated by the U. S. and the U.S.S.R. incorporate methods for the attainment of thermonuclear explosions technically different from those presented here. However, the thermonuclear physics underlying the H-bomb remains the same. Thermonuclear physics has assumed a new interest and importance to mankind in 1955 with the acknowledgment by major world powers that their atomic energy establishments are engaged in the development of means for the peaceful application of energy liberated by the fusion reactions. These two chapters are, therefore, reproduced substantially in their original form, with deletion of only a few minor technical details and of discussion of some of the political issues which are no longer timely.

THE HYDROGEN BOMB I

by Louis N. Ridenour

IN PRESIDENT TRUMAN'S first announcement of the Hiroshima atomic bomb, it was stated that the bomb drew its energy from the same source that fuels the sun and the stars. This statement is true only in the loosest sense. To be sure, a uranium-fission bomb, like the sun, derives energy from the transformation of one atomic species into others, but the types of reaction involved in the two cases are quite different.

There is excellent reason to believe that the energy source of most stars, including the sun, is a rather complicated chain of nuclear transformations whose end result is to form one atom of helium out of four atoms of hydrogen. In the sun and the stars, then, the source of energy is a chain of so-called thermonuclear reactions that ends in fusing four light hydrogen nuclei into the heavier and more complicated helium nucleus. The old-fashioned atomic bomb, on the other hand, uses as its explosive the nuclei of some of the heaviest elements known to man: uranium and plutonium. Energy is released when one of these heavy nuclei splits, or fissions, into two lighter, simpler nuclei. Thus the lightest atoms liberate energy if they are combined into heavier atoms; the heaviest atoms liberate energy when they are split into lighter ones. Only near the middle of the periodic table of the chemical elements do we find atomic species that are fully stable, in the sense that energy cannot be liberated either by combining them into heavier atoms or by splitting them into lighter ones.

To paraphrase a remark of George Gamow, we live in the midst of an atomic powder magazine, where immense amounts of energy are locked in every bit of matter. Why, then, are we safe? Why does common matter, possessed as it is of tremendous stores of energy, seem so inert, so permanent? The answer is that in order to liberate the energy of a fusion or a fission reaction we must ourselves invest some energy, just as we must expend energy to strike a match.

In the case of nuclear fission, the energy investment is small. Fission occurs when an atom of uranium 235, plutonium 239, or uranium 233 captures a neutron, even one of very slow speed. But these neutrons must be somehow produced, since they do not occur free in nature, and are in fact unstable. The nuclear "chain reaction" that is exploited in atomic bombs and in nuclear reactors like those at Hanford is possible only because the fission reaction itself releases neutrons, the very particles that are needed to keep it going.

If the lump of uranium or plutonium in which these neutrons are liberated is large enough, the neutrons released by one fission process will cause other fissions before they escape from the lump, and the process will go on faster and faster until an atomic explosion has been produced. The lump of uranium is then said to have exceeded the "critical size."

This limitation on critical size dictates the design of fission bombs. Detonation of such a bomb requires the rapid assembly of an overcritical mass; as soon as this is assembled, it blows up in about half a millionth of a second. The greatest ingenuity is needed to achieve an instantaneous condition exceeding the critical by as much as a few per cent; no amount of ingenuity has yet allowed the design of an efficient fission bomb so much as two or three times critical size. Thus there are inherently narrow limits to the size of a fission bomb: as it begins to exceed the critical, it explodes at once; if it is smaller, it cannot be exploded at all.

At the opposite end of the scale, among the light elements, the explosive conversion of mass into energy is not so easily achieved in terrestrial laboratories. To cause two light atoms to fuse into a heavier one, we must overcome powerful forces of electrical repulsion, since each nucleus is positively charged. Up to now this has been accomplished by scientists only laboriously, with poor efficiency and on an extremely small scale, by striking target atoms with a fast-moving beam of atoms accelerated in an electronuclear machine, or "atom-smasher."

In the centers of the stars, fusion reactions go on all the time, because the temperature there is some 20 million degrees centigrade. The average energy of an atom at this temperature is only some 1,700 electron volts, but some atoms have several times this energy, and collisions between atomic nuclei are so frequent that fusion reactions are produced in substantial numbers. We cannot maintain stellar temperatures on the earth, but we can produce them for very small fractions of a second. In the explosion of a uranium or plutonium bomb, the central temperature of the exploding mass has been estimated as high as 50 million degrees C. At such a temperature, fusion reactions in a dense mass of light atoms occur often enough to liberate significant amounts of energy.

Obviously the fusion reactions that are likely to be most effective for producing energy are those that will go best at relatively low collision energies, since even the highest temperatures reached in the explosion of an atomic bomb correspond to rather modest bombarding energies from the laboratory standpoint. For this reason, the stellar-energy reaction cycle is out of the question; this cycle involves the fusion of hydrogen with heavy atoms such as carbon and nitrogen, and therefore proceeds relatively slowly even at temperatures of millions of degrees. It has been known for some time, however, that fusion reactions between the rarer, heavier isotopes of hydrogen can take place much more rapidly at substantially lower temperatures. Formulas for three of these are given in the chart.

A few years ago the reaction that would have been chosen as the most promising for a hydrogen bomb was the fusion of two atoms of deuterium, or hydrogen of mass 2, containing one proton and one neutron. This results in the formation of helium 3, with the emission of a neutron and the release of about four million electron volts of energy. Gamow has calculated the thermonuclear energy release from this reaction; the results were given in his 1946 book *Atomic Energy.* He remarked that if the reaction took place at a temperature of something over one million degrees C., "a small charge of deuterium could be used as an explosive with tremendous destructive power."

Nowadays we know that a more effective reaction can be obtained with hydrogen 3, known as tritium, a radioactive but long-lived isotope of hydrogen that has one proton and two neutrons in its nucleus. Tritium not only reacts faster than deuterium at low temperatures, but also liberates more energy when it does so. A fusion reaction of tritium with deuterium produces helium 4, with the emission of a neutron; its energy yield is 17.6 million electron volts. Tritium can also fuse with tritium, yielding helium 4, two neutrons and 11.4 million electron volts of energy; the cross section for this reaction is not available in the published literature, but it is probably large.

Ponderable amounts of tritium have been and are being made by the Atomic Energy Commission in its huge facilities. The designer of a fusion bomb clearly would start with a fission bomb of uranium or plutonium, the explosion of which would produce the

Heavy hydrogen fusion reactions which might be used in an H-bomb are compared here. The atomic nuclei only are shown because, at the temperatures at which these reactions occur, atoms are stripped of their planetary electrons. Black circles signify protons, the positively charged particles which give atoms their chemical identity or atomic number, each hydrogen atom (H) having one proton and helium (He) having two. White circles signify neutrons, the electrically neutral particles which, added to the protons in the nucleus, give an atom its atomic weight or isotope number. Thus, "heavy" hydrogen or deuterium (H^2) has a proton and a neutron, and the even heavier hydrogen isotope, tritium (H^3), has a proton and two neutrons; the

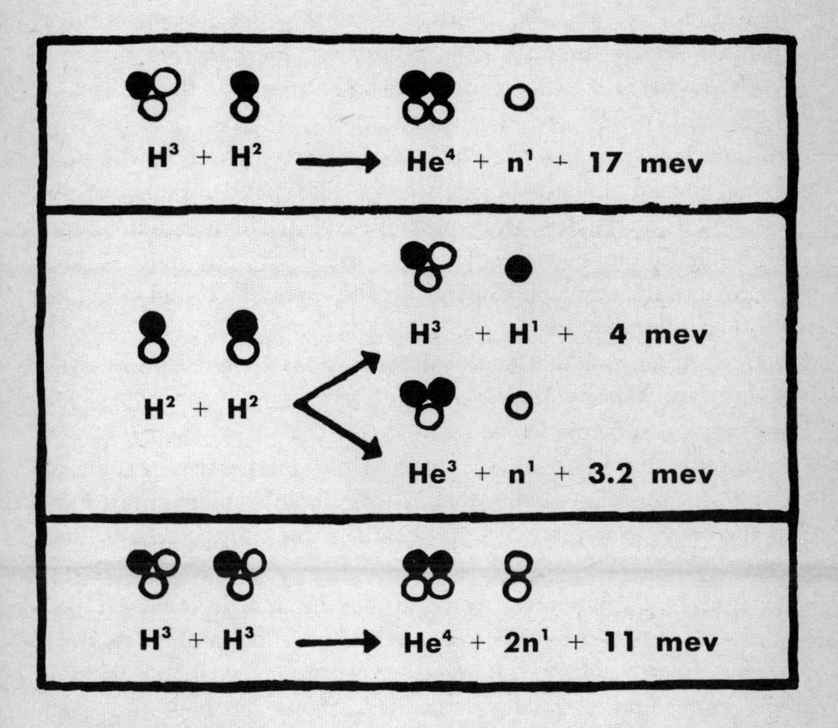

reader will see the corresponding distinction between helium (He^3) and its heavy isotope (He^4). At top, tritium is shown to react with deuterium to yield a nucleus of helium 4 plus a free neutron plus 17 million electron volts (hence "mev") of energy. The reaction of two deuterium nuclei, shown in the middle panel, may move in one of two directions. It may produce a tritium nucleus, plus a hydrogen 1 nucleus (or proton); or it may yield helium 3 nucleus plus a neutron. The energy yield in either case is about the same. The reaction of two tritium nuclei, at bottom, yields a helium 4 nucleus (or alpha particle) plus two neutrons plus 11 mev.

high temperatures required for the thermonuclear fusion reaction. To the fission bomb he would add a certain mixture of deuterium and tritium to fuel the fusion process. The final energy release of the bomb—its total deadliness—would be determined by the amount of deuterium added. To say that the fusion bomb would be 2, 7, 10, 100 or 1,000 times as devastating as the conventional fission bomb is to speak from ignorance; the effective size of a fusion bomb will depend upon the intentions and the skill of its designers.

Note, however, that there is here no concept like that of critical size. The size of the bomb depends, and depends exactly, on the amount of the reacting elements built into it. The fission detonator itself must be made overcritical in order to explode, but the happenings thereafter will depend on the amount of fuel provided for the fusion reaction.

Here, then, are the technical conclusions that one must draw about the fusion bomb:

First, it can be made.

Second, there is no limit, in principle, to the size of a fusion bomb. It cannot be smaller than a fission bomb, since it must use a fission bomb as detonator, but it can be many times, perhaps thousands of times, bigger.

Third, while fission can be controlled in an orderly way to produce useful power in a reactor, the fusion reaction offers no prospect at the present time of any use except in terms of an explosion. We cannot find in the development of the fusion bomb any such peacetime values as are inherent in the development of nuclear fission. Except where the uses of peace demand the detonation of an explosive equivalent to, say, a million tons of TNT, there is no use for a fusion reaction. Thus when we discuss the "hydrogen bomb" we are clearly speaking of a weapon, and a weapon only.

Fourth, we are speaking of a very special type of weapon—one that is appropriate only to the destruction of large targets. A weapon of this sort is clearly of much greater significance to other nations, such as the U.S.S.R., than it is to us. We have several large targets; the U.S.S.R. has only one or two.

In view of all this, it seems a little curious that the fusion bomb should have been proposed—as it apparently was—in terms of a reply to the Soviet achievement of the fission bomb. To the detached observer, it would appear to be potentially a Pyrrhic reply, involving as it does the production of a weapon uniquely suited to the destruction of the great cities around which our own economy and our own civilization are built.

THE HYDROGEN BOMB II

by Hans A. Bethe

EVERYBODY WHO TALKS about atomic energy knows Albert Einstein's equation $E = Mc^2$: viz., the energy release in a nuclear reaction can be calculated from the decrease in mass. In the fission of the uranium nucleus, one tenth of one per cent of the mass is converted into energy; in the fusion of four hydrogen nuclei to form helium, seven tenths of one per cent is so converted. When these statements are made in newspaper reports, it is usually implied that there ought to be some way in which all the mass of a nucleus could be converted into energy, and that we are merely waiting for technical developments to make this practical. Needless to say, this is wrong. Physics is sufficiently far developed to state that there will never be a way to make a proton or a neutron or any other nucleus simply disappear and convert its entire mass into energy. It is true that there are processes by which various smaller particles—positive and negative electrons and mesons—are annihilated, but all these phenomena involve at least one particle which does not normally occur in nature and therefore must first be created, and this creation process consumes as much energy as is afterwards liberated.

All the nuclear processes from which energy can be obtained involve the rearrangement of protons and neutrons in nuclei, the protons and neutrons themselves remaining intact. Hundreds of experimental investigations through the last thirty years have taught us how much energy can be liberated in each transformation, whether by the fission of heavy nuclei or the fusion of light ones. In the case of fusion, only the combination of the very lightest nuclei can release very large amounts of energy. When four hydrogen nuclei fuse to form helium, .7 per cent of the mass is transformed into energy. But if four helium nuclei were fused into oxygen, the mass would decrease by only .1 per cent; and the fusion of two silicon atoms, if it ever could occur, would release less than .02 per cent of the mass. Thus there is no prospect of using elements of medium atomic weight for the release of nuclear energy, even in theory.

The main problem in the release of nuclear energy is not the amount of energy released—this is always large enough—but whether there is a mechanism by which the release can take place at a sufficient rate. This consideration is almost invariably ignored by science reporters, who seem to be incurably fascinated by $E = Mc^2$. In fusion the rate of reaction is governed by entirely different factors from those in fission. Fission takes place when a nucleus of uranium or plutonium captures a neutron. Because the neutron has no electric charge and is not repelled by the nucleus, temperature has no important influence on the fission reaction; no matter how slow the neutron, it can enter a uranium nucleus and cause fission. In fusion reactions, on the other hand, two nuclei, both with positive electric charges, must come into contact. To overcome their strong mutual electrical repulsion, the nuclei must move at each other with great speed. Ridenour explained how this is achieved in the laboratory by giving very high velocities to a few nuclei. This method is inefficient because it is highly unlikely that one of the fast projectiles will hit a target nucleus before it is slowed down by the many collisions with the electrons also present in the atoms of the target.

The only known way that energy can be extracted from light nuclei by fusion is by thermonuclear reactions, i.e., those which proceed at exceedingly high temperatures. The prime example of such reactions occurs in the interior of stars, where temperatures are of the order of 20 million degrees centigrade. At this temperature the average energy of an atom is still only 1,700 electron volts—much less than the energies given to nuclear particles in "atom smashers." But all the particles present—nuclei and electrons—have high kinetic energy, so they are not slowed down by colliding with one another. They will keep their high speeds. Nevertheless, in spite of the high temperature, the nuclear reactions in stars proceed at an extremely slow rate; only one per cent of the hydrogen in the sun is transformed into helium in a billion years. Indeed, it would be catastrophic for the star if the reaction went much faster.

The temperature at the center of a star is kept high and very nearly constant by an interplay of a number of physical forces. The radiation produced by nuclear reactions in the interior can escape from the star only with great difficulty. It proceeds to the surface not in a straight line but by a complicated, zigzag route, since it is constantly absorbed by atoms and re-emitted in new directions. It is this slow escape of radiation that maintains the high interior temperature, which in turn maintains the thermonuclear reactions. Only a star large enough to hold its radiations for a long time can produce significant amounts of energy. The sun's radiation, for example, takes about 10,000 years to escape. A star weighing one-

Possible hydrogen fusion reactions are charted here to illustrate an important consideration in design of a hydrogen bomb. The various reactions as shown here may be understood by reference to the caption on page 164, which explains the graphic symbols and the most significant of these reactions. The middle column gives the energy yield of each reaction, expressed in millions of electron volts, or mev. The column at right gives the time required for each reaction at exceedingly high temperatures such as are generated by a fission bomb. It can be seen that the heavy hydrogen reactions proceed at a much faster rate. Since it is difficult to maintain the necessary temperatures for more than a brief instant on earth, the heavy hydrogen reactions are likely to be preferred. Among these, it can be seen that the tritium-deuterium reaction not only yields the greatest energy, but requires the briefest instant of time.

Reaction	Energy	Time
$H^1 + H^1 \rightarrow H^2 + \overset{+}{e}$	1.4 mev	10^{11} YEARS
 $H^2 + H^1 \rightarrow He^3 + h\nu$	5 mev	.5 SECOND
$H^3 + H^1 \rightarrow He^4 + h\nu$	20 mev	.05 SECOND
$H^2 + H^2 \rightarrow He^3 + n^1$	3.2 mev	.00003 SECOND
$H^2 + H^2 \rightarrow H^3 + H^1$	4 mev	.00003 SECOND
$H^3 + H^2 \rightarrow He^4 + n^1$	17 mev	.0000012 SECOND
 $H^3 + H^3 \rightarrow He^4 + n^1 + n^1$	11 mev	?

tenth as much as the sun would produce so little energy that it would not be visible, and the largest planet, Jupiter, is already so small that it could not maintain nuclear reactions at all. This rules out the possibility that the earth's atmosphere, or the ocean, or the earth's crust, could be set "on fire" by a hydrogen superbomb and the earth thus be converted into a star. Because of the small mass of the bomb, it would heat only a small volume of the earth or its atmosphere, and even if nuclear reactions were started, radiation would carry away the nuclear energy much faster than it developed, and the temperature would drop rapidly so that the nuclear reaction would soon stop.

If thermonuclear reactions are to be initiated on earth, one must take into consideration that any nuclear energy released will be carried away rapidly by radiation, so that it will not be possible to keep the temperature high for a long time. Therefore, if the reaction is to proceed at all, it must proceed very quickly. Reaction times of billions of years, like those in the sun, would never lead to an appreciable energy release; we must think rather in terms of millionths of a second. On the other hand, on earth we have a choice of materials: whereas the stellar reactions can use only the elements that happen to be abundant in stars, notably ordinary hydrogen, we can choose any elements we like for our thermonuclear reactions. We shall obviously choose those with the highest reaction rates; the range of our choice is indicated in the accompanying table.

The reaction rate depends first of all, and extremely sensitively, on the product of the charges of the reacting nuclei; the smaller this product, the higher the reaction rate. The highest rates will therefore be obtainable from a reaction between two hydrogen nuclei, because hydrogen has the smallest possible charge—one unit. (The principal reactions in stars are between carbon, of charge six, and hydrogen.) We can choose any of the three hydrogen isotopes, of atomic weight one (proton), two (deuteron) or three (triton). These isotopes undergo different types of nuclear reactions, and the reactions occur at different rates.

The fusion of two protons is called the proton-proton reaction. It has long been known that this reaction is exceedingly slow; the proton-proton reaction takes 100 billion years to occur at the center of the sun. Ridenour points out that the situation is quite different for the reactions using only the heavy isotopes of hydrogen: the deuteron and triton. A number of reported measurements by nuclear physicists have shown that the reaction rates for this type of fusion are high.

What would be the effects of a hydrogen bomb? Ridenour notes that its power would be limited only by the amount of heavy hydrogen that could be carried in the bomb. A bomb carried by a submarine, for instance, could be much more powerful than one carried by a plane. Let us assume an H-bomb releasing 1,000 times as much energy as the Hiroshima bomb. The radius of destruction by blast from a bomb increases as the cube root of the increase in the bomb's power. At Hiroshima the radius of severe destruction was one mile. So an H-bomb would cause almost complete destruction of buildings up to a radius of ten miles. By the blast effect alone a single bomb could obliterate almost all of Greater New York or Moscow or London or any of the largest cities of the world. But this is not all; we must also consider the heat effects. About 30 per cent of the casualties in Hiroshima were caused by flash burns due to the intense burst of heat radiation from the bomb. Fatal burns were frequent up to distances of 4,000 to 5,000 feet. The radius of heat radiation increases with power at a higher rate than that of blast, namely by the square root of the power instead of the cube root. Thus the H-bomb would widen the range of fatal heat by a factor of 30; it would burn people to death over a radius of up to 20 miles or more. It is too easy to put down or read numbers without understanding them; one must visualize what it would mean if, for instance, Chicago with all its suburbs and most of their inhabitants were wiped out in a single flash.

In addition to blast and heat radiation there are nuclear radiations. Some of these are instantaneous; they are emitted by the exploding bomb itself and may be absorbed by the bodies of persons in the bombed area. Others are delayed; these come from the radioactive nuclei formed as a consequence of the nuclear explosion, and they may be confined to the explosion area or widely dispersed. The bombs, both A and H, emit gamma rays and neutrons while they explode. Either of these radiations can enter the body and cause death or radiation sickness. It is likely, however, that most of the people who would get a lethal dose of radiation from the H-bomb would be killed in any case by flash burn or by collapsing or burning buildings.

There would also be persistent radioactivity. This is of two kinds: the fission products formed in the bomb itself, and the radioactive atoms formed in the environment by the neutrons emitted from the bomb. Since the H-bomb must be triggered by an A-bomb, it will produce at least as many fission products as an A-bomb alone. The neutrons produced by the fusion reactions may greatly increase the radioactive effect. They would be absorbed by the bomb case, by rocks and other material on the ground, and by the air. The bomb case could be so designed that it would become highly radioactive when disintegrated by the explosion.* These radioactive atoms would then be carried by the wind over a large area of the bombed country. The radioactive nuclei formed on the ground

* It is this radioactivity of the bomb case which bulked largest in the fall-out after one of the U. S. H-bomb tests in the Pacific in 1954. The U. S. Atomic Energy Commission has estimated that the fall-out from the detonation of an H-bomb of present design might produce lethal radioactivity (more than 500 roentgen units) over an area of about 7,000 square miles. Persons in the fall-out area may be protected by staying in an appropriate shelter for several days, and then evacuating.

would contaminate the center of the bombed area for some time, but probably not for very long because the constituents of soil and buildings do not form many long-lived radioactive nuclei by neutron capture. Neutrons released in the air are finally captured by nitrogen nuclei, which are thereby transformed into radioactive carbon 14. This isotope, however, has a long half-life—5,000 years—and therefore its radioactivity is relatively weak.

The decision to proceed with the development of hydrogen bombs has been made. I believe that this decision settles only one question and raises a hundred in its place. What will the bomb do to our strategic position? Will it restore to us the superiority in armament that we possessed before the Russians obtained the A-bomb? Will it improve our chances of winning the next war if one should come? Will it diminish the likelihood that we should see our cities destroyed in that war? Will it serve to avert or postpone war itself? How will the world look after a war fought with hydrogen bombs?

I believe the most important question is the moral one: Can we, who have always insisted on morality and human decency between nations as well as inside our own country, introduce this weapon of total annihilation into the world? Whoever wishes to use the hydrogen bomb in our conflict with the U.S.S.R., either as a threat or in actual warfare, is adhering to the old fallacy that the ends justify the means. The fallacy is the more obvious because our conflict with the U.S.S.R. is mainly about means. It is the means that the U.S.S.R. is using, both in dealing with her own citizens and with other nations, that we abhor; we have little quarrel with the professed aim of providing a decent standard of living for all. We would invalidate our cause if we were to use in our fight means that can only be termed mass slaughter.

We believe in personal liberty and human dignity, the value and importance of the individual, sincerity and openness in the dealings between men and between nations. All this is in great contrast to the methods which the Soviet Government uses in pursuing its aims and which it believes necessary in the "beginning phase" of Communism—which by now has lasted thirty-three years. We believe in peace based on mutual trust. Shall we achieve it by using hydrogen bombs? Shall we convince the Russians of the value of the individual by killing millions of them? If we fight a war and win it with H-bombs, what history will remember is not the ideals we were fighting for but the methods we used to accomplish them.

What would an all-out war fought with hydrogen bombs mean? It would mean the obliteration of all large cities and probably of many smaller ones, and the killing of most of their inhabitants. After such a war, nothing that resembled present civilization would remain. The fight for mere survival would dominate everything. The destruction of the cities might set technology back a hundred years or more. In a generation even the knowledge of technology and science might disappear, because there would be no opportunity to practice them. Indeed it is likely that technology and science, having brought such utter misery upon man, would be suspected as works of the devil, and that a new Dark Age would begin on earth.

It is ironical that the U. S. of all countries should lead in developing such methods of warfare. The military methods adopted by this nation at the outset of the Second World War had the aim of conserving lives as much as possible. Determined not to repeat the slaughter of the First World War, during which hundreds of thousands of soldiers were sacrificed in fruitless frontal attacks, the U. S. high command substituted war by machines for war by unprotected men. But the hydrogen bomb carries mechanical warfare to ultimate absurdity in defeating its own aim. Instead of saving lives, it takes many more lives; in place of one soldier who would die in battle, it kills a hundred noncombatant civilians. Surely it is time for us to reconsider what our real intentions are.

One may well ask: Why advance such arguments with reference

to the H-bomb and not atomic bombs in general? Is an atomic bomb moral and a hydrogen bomb immoral, and if so, where is the dividing line? I believe there was a deep feeling in this country right after the war that the use of atomic bombs in Japan had been a mistake, and that these bombs should be eliminated from national armaments. This feeling, indeed, was one of the prime reasons for President Truman's offer of international control in 1945. We know that the negotiations for control have not led to success as yet. But our inability to eliminate atomic bombs is no reason to introduce a bomb which is a thousand times worse.

When atomic bombs were first introduced, there was a general feeling that they represented something new, that the thousandfold increase of destructive power from blockbuster to atom bomb required and made possible a new approach. The step from atomic to hydrogen bombs is just as great again, so we have again an equally strong reason to seek a new approach. We have to think how we can save humanity from this ultimate disaster. And we must break the habit, which seems to have taken hold of this nation, of considering every weapon as just another piece of machinery and a fair means to win our struggle with the U.S.S.R.

I have reviewed the moral issues that should deter us from using hydrogen bombs even if we were sure that we alone would have them, and that they would contribute to our victory. The true situation is rather the reverse; we can hardly hope to keep a monopoly on hydrogen bombs. When the time comes that both the U. S. and the U.S.S.R. have this weapon, we shall be more vulnerable than the Russians. We have many more large cities that would be inviting targets, and many of these lie near the coast so that they could be reached by submarine and perhaps a relatively short-range rocket.

But, say the advocates of the bomb, what if the Russians obtain the H-bomb first? I doubt that the hydrogen bomb, dreadful as it would be, could win a war in one stroke. Though it might devastate our cities and cripple our ability to conduct a long war with all modern weapons, it would not seriously affect our power for immediate retaliation. Our atomic bombs, whether "old style" or hydrogen, and our planes would presumably be so distributed that they could not all be wiped out at the same time; they would still be ready to take off and reduce the country of the aggressor to at least the same state as our own. Thus the large bomb would bring untold destruction but no decision. I believe that "old-fashioned" A-bombs would be sufficient to even the score in case of an initial Soviet attack with H-bombs on this country. In fact, because of the greater number available, A-bombs may well be more effective in destroying legitimate military targets, including production centers. H-bombs, after all, would be useful only against the largest targets, of which there are very few in the U.S.S.R.

So we come finally to one reason, and only one, that can justify our building the H-bomb: namely, to deter the Russians from using it against us, if only for fear of retaliation.*

* The development started in 1950 has now been completed. A test of a large thermonuclear "device" was announced by the U. S. in 1952, another by the U.S.S.R. in 1953. Fear of retaliation has become the cornerstone of military policy on both sides. At present, and especially here in Geneva in the atmosphere of the International Conference on the Peaceful Uses of Atomic Energy, the political scene looks brighter. Nevertheless, if ever a general war should come, it is likely that H-bombs will be used, if not at the beginning, then during the course of the war. This possibility menaces the continued existence of civilization. Whatever agreements the nations may conclude to minimize this menace, it is no longer in our power to go back to a world without H-bombs.

August, 1955 H. A. B.
Geneva, Switzerland

BIBLIOGRAPHY

READERS interested in further reading on atomic power may find the list below helpful. It is *not* a bibliography of source material. The titles chosen are for the most part addressed to the general reader; they include also some of the more accessible textbooks, survey volumes and government bulletins. The list is by no means exhaustive. Nor does it cover all of the topics in this book, since much of the work reported here is not yet represented in the pages of any other book. (The date given in italics under each chapter title is the date of its original publication in SCIENTIFIC AMERICAN.)

THE NUCLEAR REACTOR
July 1949

Atomic Energy Development: Fifth Semiannual Report of the United States Atomic Energy Commission, 1947–1948. United States Government Printing Office, 1948.

Explaining the Atom. Selig Hecht. Viking Press, 1947. Revised Edition (Eugene Rabinowitch), 1954.

Atomic Energy. Henry D. Smyth. Princeton University Press, 1945.

RESEARCH REACTORS
April 1951

The Science and Engineering of Nuclear Power, Vols. I and II. Clark D. Goodman. Addison-Wesley Press, Inc., 1947 and 1949.

THE BREEDER REACTOR
December 1952

"Basic Problems in Central-Station Nuclear Power." W. H. Zinn in *Nucleonics,* Vol. 10, No. 9. September, 1952.

POWER REACTORS
December 1954

Elements of Nuclear Reactor Theory. Samuel Glasstone and Milton C. Edlund. D. Van Nostrand Company, Inc., 1952.

Introduction to Nuclear Engineering. Richard Stephenson. McGraw-Hill Book Company, Inc., 1954.

THE GENEVA CONFERENCE
October 1955

Report on the Atom. Gordon Dean. Alfred A. Knopf, 1953.

THE EARTH'S URANIUM
May 1951

"Geology of the Fissionable Materials." George W. Bain in *Economic Geology*, Vol. 45, No. 4, pages 273–323. June-July, 1950.

URANIUM FROM COAL
October 1954

"Recent Estimates of the Abundances of the Elements in the Earth's Crust." Michael Fleischer. *U. S. Geological Survey Circular 313.*

"Results of Reconnaissance for Uraniferous Coal, Lignite and Carbonaceous Shale in Western Montana." W. J. Hail, Jr., and J. R. Gill. *U. S. Geological Survey Circular 251.*

REACTOR CHEMISTRY
July 1952

Sourcebook on Atomic Energy. Samuel Glasstone. D. Van Nostrand Company, Inc., 1950.

FISSION PRODUCTS
June 1952

Industrial Uses of Radioactive Fission Products. Stanford Research Institute. September, 1951.

THE PRICE PER KILOWATT-HOUR
January 1951

Economic Aspects of Atomic Power. An Exploratory Study under the Direction of Sam H. Schurr and Jacob Marschak. Princeton University Press, 1950.

THE ATOMIC ENERGY ACT OF 1954
November 1954

Atomic Energy Act of 1954. U. S. Government Printing Office, 1954.
The Control of Atomic Energy. James R. Newman and Byron S. Miller. McGraw-Hill Book Company, Inc., 1948.

INTERNATIONAL CO-OPERATION
April 1955

Britain's Atomic Factories. K. E. B. Jay. H. M. Stationery Office, 1954.
Report on the Atom. Gordon Dean. Alfred A. Knopf, 1953.
Major Activities in the Atomic Energy Program. Semiannual Report of the Atomic Energy Commission to Congress, August-December, 1954. Government Printing Office, 1955.

THE LETHAL EFFECTS OF RADIATION
December 1951

Actions of Radiations on Living Cells. Douglas E. Lea. Cambridge University Press, 1947.

TRACERS
February 1949

Radioactive Tracers in Biology. M. D. Kamen. Academic Press, 1948.

THE HYDROGEN BOMB I
March 1950

Atomic Energy. George Gamow. Cambridge University Press, 1946.

THE HYDROGEN BOMB II
April 1950

Elementary Nuclear Theory. H. A. Bethe. John Wiley & Son, Inc., 1947.